INTRODUCTION

to the

MATHEMATICS

of

DEMOGRAPHY

(Second Edition)

Robert L. Brown, FSA, FCIA, ACAS

ACTEX Publications
Winsted, Connecticut

Manufactured in the United States of America

10 9 8 7 6 5 4 3 2

Cover design by MUF

Library of Congress Cataloging-in-Publication Data

Brown, Robert L., 1949-
    Introduction to the mathematics of demography / Robert L. Brown
        p.   cm.
    Includes bibliographical references and index.
    ISBN 0-936031-08-5
    1. Demography--Mathematical models.   I. Title.
HB849.51.B76   1991
304.6'01'5118--dc20   91-13446
                                                                CIP

ISBN 0-936031-14-X

TABLE OF
CONTENTS

PREFACE

In spite of an increased interest and publication activity in the general subject area of demography, a major void still remains: a suitable textbook to introduce undergraduate students to the mathematics of demography.

Textbooks and journal papers on the topic of demography will typically have one of two basic foundational sources. Many find their basis in sociology, and are almost entirely descriptive and qualitative in presentation. Then there is a wide variety of texts and papers written from a mathematical perspective, but these are often either devoid of the descriptive material necessary for a sound pedagogical presentation, or they are advanced works more suitable for graduate courses.

This text, appropriately called *Introduction to the Mathematics of Demography*, tries to strike a happy compromise between a qualitative presentation and introductory, undergraduate quantitative analysis. There is much material that is purely descriptive, but there is also an extensive survey of the foundational mathematics required in much of the work done by demographers. The mathematical content can be understood by undergraduate students with a background of algebra, introductory calculus, and introductory probability.

Examples are drawn from North American applications and studies. Each chapter includes a number of worked examples and a set of exercises for the reader to solve. Many of the text exercises appeared on recent Course 161 examinations given by the Society of Actuaries. Their permission to include these question in the text is greatly appreciated.

The author wishes to acknowledge the heavy influence on this text of predecessor works by Keyfitz [15], Pollard, Yusuf, and

Pollard [22], and Keyfitz and Beekman [16]. The last was especially important, as many of this text's examples and problems arose from similar problems presented earlier in that text.

The author wishes to thank a number of professionals who reviewed several drafts of the text and made valuable contributions to the finished product. Notable among these persons are Jeffrey A. Beckley, FSA, Beckley & Associates, Inc.; John A. Beekman, ASA, Ph.D., Ball State University; Richard Bilisoly, FSA, Society of Actuaries; James C. Hickman, FSA, Ph.D., University of Wisconsin; Robert Hupf, FSA, Mutual of Omaha Insurance Company; Bertram M. Kestenbaum, ASA, Social Security Administration; Richard F. Lambert, FSA, Prudential Insurance Company of America; and Elias S. Shiu, ASA, Ph.D., University of Manitoba.

Special thanks to Alice H. Wade, ASA, Social Security Administration, who, as chairperson of the Society of Actuaries Course 161 Examination Committee, was very supportive of the project and coordinated the manuscript review efforts of the committee members. Thanks also to Ms. Wade for supplying the U.S. Life Tables which appear in Appendix A.

Finally the author expresses his appreciation to the people at ACTEX Publications, who turned a rough manuscript into a finished textbook. The principle players on that team included Marilyn J. Baleshiski, format and layout editor, Sandi Lynn Fratini, style editor, Dick London, FSA, mathematics editor, and Marlene F. Lundbeck, cover and graphic arts.

While the contributions of the above-named persons are sincerely acknowledged, the author takes full responsibility for any remaining errors or deficiencies in the text.

Robert L. Brown, FSA, FCIA, ACAS
University of Waterloo
Waterloo, Ontario
April 1991

PREFACE TO THE SECOND EDITION

In the two years that have passed since the publication of *Introduction to the Mathematics of Demography*, classroom use of the text by the author and others has revealed the need for some important revisions. These revisions are in the nature of improvements in presentation rather than in content. Thus the Second Edition covers substantially the same material that was covered in the original text, but has clarified and improved the presentation in many areas.

In Chapter 1, the presentation of Myers' blending technique has been improved through an example, and an appendix has been added showing the derivation of the formula for the standard error of estimate in a one-in-six sample. In Chapter 4, an example has been added to clarify the higher-age extrapolation procedure used in constructing the U.S. Life Tables, an issue that has perplexed students in this area for years.

The introductory presentation of stationary and stable population theory, in Chapters 5 and 6, respectively, has been completely rewritten to provide a clearer understanding of those models. In particular, the nature of the stationary model as a special case of the stable model has been more clearly shown.

Throughout the text an effort has been made to attain consistency in notation for similar concepts, and, conversely, to use different notation for sufficiently different concepts. For example, the new edition now uses b_c for the crude birth rate of a population, which is a statistic of actual data, and b_i for the intrinsic birth rate of a stable population, which is a parameter of a mathematical model. The original text unwisely used the symbol b for both concepts. Other examples of notational improvement can be found by readers familiar with both editions of the text.

We believe the improvements contained in the new edition will further the ability of the text to attain its goal of providing a clear introduction to the mathematics of demography.

RLB
April 1993

CHAPTER 1

DATA: SOURCES AND ERRORS

1.1 INTRODUCTION

Demography is a term derived from two Greek words, which, if translated literally, means "*to draw or write about people.*" According to the United Nations Multilingual Demographic Dictionary, "*Demography is the scientific study of human populations, primarily with respect to their size, their structure, and their development.*" A more precise definition, given by Bogue, is as follows:

> "*Demography is the statistical and mathematical study of the size, composition, and spatial distribution of human populations, and of changes over time in these aspects through the operation of the five processes of fertility, mortality, marriage, migration, and social mobility*" ([2], p. 1).

Mathematical demography had its beginnings in the development of procedures for the formation of life tables (see Chapters 3 and 4). The 1662 work by John Graunt, *Natural and Political Observations Upon the Bills of Mortality* (see Keyfitz and Smith [18], pp. 11-20), is cited as the first substantive demographic work to be published. Graunt was able to derive an impressive array of demographic information using only lists of christenings and deaths during the time of the London plague. A portion of Graunt's report is illustrated in Table 1.1 on the following page.

A second work of importance in mathematical demography was the Breslau Table of 1693, a life table developed by Edmund Halley, after whom Halley's comet is named. (See Keyfitz and Smith [18], pp. 21-26.)

TABLE 1.1

Table of Notorious Diseases		Table of Causalities	
Apoplexy	1306	Bleeding	9
Cut of the Stone	38	Burnt and Scalded	125
Falling Sickness	74	Drowned	829
Dead in the Streets	243	Excessive drinking	2
Gowt	134	Frighted	22
Headache	51	Grief	279
Jaundice	998	Hanged themselves	222
Lethargy	67	Killed by several	
Leprosy	6	accidents	1021
Lunatick	158	Murdered	86
Overlaid and Starved	529	Poisoned	14
Palsy	423	Smothered	26
Rupture	201	Shot	17
Stone and Strangury	863	Starved	51
Sciatica	5	Vomiting	136
Sodainly	454		

Another important step in the development of mathematical demography was the publication in 1798 of *An Essay on the Principle of Population* by Reverend Thomas Robert Malthus. He postulated that human populations would naturally increase faster than the food supply needed to sustain them. Malthus believed that what kept the population at a sustainable level were checks that he categorized as vice, misery, and moral restraint. Vices which controlled population growth were wars and excesses of all kinds. The misery category included diseases, epidemics, famine, plague, and so on.

1.2   THE COLLECTION OF DEMOGRAPHIC STATISTICS

Virtually all basic demographic data come from censuses, surveys, or vital statistics registration systems.

A *census* (from the Latin *censere*, to assess) has been defined as *"the total process of collecting, compiling and publishing demographic, economic, and social data pertaining, at a specified time or times, to all persons of a defined territory."* An in-depth discussion of census-taking follows by looking at how the United States and Canada take a census and what is produced.

A census may be taken on either a *de facto* or a *de jure* basis. Under the *de facto* method, persons are counted wherever they are at the time of the census. Under the *de jure* method, persons are counted according to their usual place of residence, so that those temporarily absent would be counted as if at home.

Both Canada and the United States use the *de jure* method, except in the case of transients where the *de facto* method applies. In the rest of the world, the *de facto* method is more common and is recommended by the United Nations Population Commission.

The advantage of the *de jure* method is that it gives a picture of the permanent population of the communities enumerated. This information could be used, for example, to determine how many political representatives that jurisdiction should have.

The disadvantage of the *de jure* method is that some persons may be omitted from the count, since they are absent from their usual residence, or could be counted twice, once at their temporary residence and again at their usual residence. Further, information secured secondhand about persons who are temporarily absent may be incomplete or incorrect.

Conversely, the main advantage of the *de facto* method is that it offers less chance of double-counting or omission of persons. The disadvantages of the *de facto* method are threefold: it is difficult to obtain information about persons in transit, it provides an incorrect picture of the usual population of a community, and vital statistic rates may be distorted because the population base is not relative to the vital statistics (*e.g.*, persons normally return to their usual residence for the birth of a child).

In Canada and the United States, most census forms are mailed out, one per household, and mailed back. The head of the household will usually answer the questions for all members of that household. In countries with lower literacy levels, each individual is interviewed by a trained enumerator or canvasser.

An advantage of the mail-out approach is that the census can be taken on one particular day. The use of enumerators usually means that the census must be spread out over several days or weeks. This may lead to problems with respect to births, deaths, and migration during that period of time. If the time lapse is prolonged, it may also lead to inaccuracies because of poor memory.

Surveys are used to discover certain errors in the census (see Section 1.4), to provide information between censuses at more frequent intervals, and to provide information on topics not included in the census. For example, the monthly sample surveys conducted by the Census Bureau in the United States and by Statistics Canada provide data on monthly labor force statistics, including unemployment rates.

Sample surveys contain errors of coverage, classification, and sampling error, which will be discussed in detail later (see Section 1.4). While these surveys are usually very accurate on a national basis, they should be used with care on a sub-national basis. Each survey publication should indicate the accuracy of the data. Users of the survey are advised to review this information carefully in order to understand the limits of the presentation. All definitions should be carefully checked so that the terms used are clearly understood. This is especially true for data analysis done by agencies other than the Census Bureau or Statistics Canada. Terms in the data published by other agencies are commonly used incorrectly, such as the use of the term rate in place of ratio (see Chapter 2).

The term *vital statistics* generally refers to data regarding vital events such as birth, adoption, death, marriage, divorce, legal separation, and annulment. By legal requirement the data are usually recorded at the time of the occurrence of the event. The registration of these events is a provincial responsibility in Canada. In the United States, each state has the responsibility for the registration of its own vital statistics. The cities of Baltimore, New Orleans, and New York maintain systems independent of the states in which they are located.

In some instances, vital statistics are combined with census data for certain reports, such as the Life Tables of the United States and Canada. For example, the 1979-81 U.S. National Life Tables combine mortality data from state registries for the period of 1979 to 1981 and compare it to the census population of April 1, 1980. This combination derives a central death rate at each age. A similar combination of data is used in the 1985-87 Canadian Life Tables.

A *population register* is a system of continuous registration with an entry for each individual. Population registers are used by a number of countries, including Netherlands, Belgium, Finland, Sweden, Norway, Denmark, Iceland, Italy, Gibraltar, Germany, Israel, Japan, Taiwan, the U.S.S.R., Bulgaria, and Czechoslovakia.

Population registers are useful in providing a permanent up-to-date data base for legal identification of persons, elections, military service, and so on. Special studies can be done by choosing appropriate samples of the data. On the negative side, population registers are expensive to maintain and may become defective. They are usually used only in countries with a high literacy rate and low migration.

Finally, data on immigrants and emigrants are usually collected at the point of their entry or exit, such as an airport. This presumes legal migration. The number of illegal immigrants into the United States makes statistics on migration there less credible.

1.3 TAKING THE CENSUS

There are indications of population enumerations being made as early as 3800 B.C. in Babylonia and 3000 B.C. in China. The first census in North America was taken in New France (Quebec) in 1666 by Jean Talon. Decennial censuses have been taken in the United States since 1790 and in Canada since 1851. Canada has also taken a smaller quinquennial census since 1956. The Canadian census takes place on June 1, and the U.S. census takes place on April 1. These dates are chosen to maximize the number of people at home at their normal residence (the *de jure* method) while being close to midyear.

In Canada, the census, and several other demographic surveys, are the responsibility of Statistics Canada. In the United States, the census is the responsibility of the Census Bureau, which is a part of the Department of Commerce. In addition to taking the decennial Census of Population and Housing, the Census Bureau conducts the Economic Censuses, a Census of Agriculture, and a Census of Governments every five years. The Bureau also conducts hundreds of surveys, some as often as once a month.

The U.S. Census is required by law, under Article 1, Section 2 of the Constitution, to ensure representation in the House of Representatives by population size. However, the census is designed to satisfy the needs of a broad range of possible users. While keeping the questions the same from census to census enhances continuity and comparative statistics, the questions posed change slightly in every census. The number of questions posed is a compromise between the needs of users and the cost of collecting and processing the information. Both the Census Bureau and

Statistics Canada expend considerable energy trying to optimize the questions to be asked so as to satisfy as many users as possible within budgetary constraints.

Both Canada and the United States widely pretest the census questions and census forms before the actual census, and provide extensive publicity at the time of the census. Both countries also provide telephone backup to the census, whereby individuals can phone in toll-free to seek guidance with the questionnaire. Complete confidentiality of individual information is guaranteed. No one can get data from the census bureau that would allow identification of any individual information.

To optimize the collection of a wide database, while limiting the overall cost, both Canada and the United States use *sampling techniques* whereby not every household answers every question.

In the 1986 Canadian census, 80% of the households in urban areas were given a short form that asked questions as to name, date of birth, sex, marital status, aboriginal status, mother tongue, type of dwelling, and dwelling ownership. The other 20% of urban households, and all rural and northern households, were given the long form which repeated all of the questions from the short form, but also included questions on labor force activity, income, education, disability, citizenship, housing (energy use and shelter costs), ethnicity, and language.

The 1990 United States census included a short form questionnaire that approximately five out of every six urban households in the nation received. The short form asked 14 questions, of which 7 applied to each person, 6 applied to housing conditions, and the final was a control question to assure that all household members were counted and no visitors were counted. A random sample of approximately 1 in 6 urban households received a long form of the questionnaire that asked these questions, and an additional 19 questions about housing conditions and 26 additional questions about each individual. Several of these questions had multiple parts, but it was not necessary for everyone to answer every question. Some questions applied only to households or persons with certain characteristics.

In smaller towns and counties (less than 2500 in population) one out of every two households received the long form. The 50% sample rate was used in areas that constituted approximately one-tenth of the nation's population. In total, about 81% of the population completed the short form, and 19% completed the long form.

Both the United States and Canada have used a combination of *mail-out/mail-back* and *enumerators*. For example, in the 1990 United States census, the Postal Service delivered census questionnaires to about 83% of all addresses in the country, primarily in metropolitan areas. For another 11% of the nation's housing units, mostly in rural and seasonal-housing areas, enumerators visited every housing unit before census day, and left a census questionnaire to be completed and returned by mail. In sparsely populated parts of the country, where it is often difficult to determine mailing addresses and not cost effective for enumerators to drop off questionnaires, the Postal Service delivered unaddressed questionnaires to all known housing units. Members of these households were to complete the forms and hold them for collection by enumerators. Enumerators recorded the addresses when they picked up the questionnaires. This technique applied to only about 6% of all households but covered 50% of the nation's land area.

1.4 SOURCES OF ERRORS AND THEIR CORRECTIONS

Census and vital statistics have several sources of error which we will now discuss in some detail.

1.4.1 Coverage Errors

Every effort is made to minimize coverage errors (*e.g.*, missing a dwelling) but errors do occur. Sometimes errors lead to double counting or *overcoverage*, although this is usually much less of a problem than *undercoverage*, which occurs when individuals or households are missed.

The primary program for measuring undercoverage is the *Post Enumeration Program*. This program involves several post enumeration surveys that attempt to measure the quality of the census data. In addition to measuring undercoverage, the program tries to measure the number of persons erroneously included in the census, (such as babies born after April 1), persons counted more than once, and persons coded to the wrong geographic area.

The Bureau combines results from these surveys to form an estimate of the net undercount or net overcount. The combined samples from the surveys are large enough to permit publication of relatively reliable data at the state level.

Another method used to quantify the census undercount or overcount is to estimate the expected result of the census count by building up the population from the last census count with births, deaths, and immigration. This method can be formulated as

$$P(t) = P(0) + B - D + I - E, \qquad (1.1)$$

where $P(t)$ is the predicted population at time t, B is the births in the period, D is the deaths in the period, I is the immigrants in the period, and E is the emigrants in the period. The excess of the actual census count over the predicted census count, divided by the actual count, is called the *error of closure.*

According to this method, the U.S. census missed 3.3% of the population in 1950, 2.6% in 1960, and 2.3% in 1970. In 1980, the component approach given by Equation (1.1) yielded an estimate of about 226 million for the true population of legal residents. The final 1980 census count was roughly 226.5 million, showing a significant improvement in coverage. Estimates are not yet available for the 1990 census.

Undercoverage might not be of widespread concern if it were random among population groups or geographic areas. Evaluations in previous censuses, however, have indicated that undercoverage varies in some specific regions and groups. These errors can seriously affect the federal and state funding provided to major U.S. cities, such as New York.

1.4.2 Content or Response Errors

Sometimes it proves impossible to obtain a complete response from a household, even if the dwelling was identified as occupied and a questionnaire was dropped off. The household members may be away during the entire census period, or the members may refuse to complete the form even though required by law. More often, the questionnaire is returned but information is missing for some questions or some individuals.

Census enumerators in the United States and census representatives in Canada are responsible for seeing that questionnaires are completed for every address in their area. Where questionnaires arrive with missing information, enumerators phone or visit the households until all questions have been answered.

Some nonresponse is inevitable, and although certain adjustments for missing data can be made during processing, some loss of accuracy must follow.

After detecting response errors, values for missing or incomplete entries are imputed. *Imputation* can be by *allocation* or *substitution*. When omissions are completed by inferring the correct value from other questionnaire answers, it is referred to as an allocation. An example would be a missing marital status for a 19-year-old son that is filled in as single because a 22-year-old son was also reported as single. This is also called the *deterministic* approach. A substitution, on the other hand, selects a record that has a number of characteristics in common with the record that is missing or in error, and imputes the missing information from this "donor" record. For example, suppose a housing unit is reported as occupied, but no other information is given. The full set of information for that unit would be taken from a similar "donor" unit. The method of substitution is also referred to as the *probabilistic* approach. The imputation procedure accounted for approximately 761,000 persons out of a final count of 226.5 million in the 1980 Census (.34% of the total). Similar statistics are not yet available for the 1990 Census.

In general, the higher the allocation rate the more variance one can expect in the data. Allocations may also introduce bias in the data, if, on average, characteristics of nonrespondents differ from those of respondents (*e.g.*, income level).

The Bureau gets a measure of response errors by means of content evaluation studies, including a reinterview of about 12,000 long-form housing units. The Bureau compares the results with the responses recorded in the basic records of the census.

1.4.3 Misstatement of Age

Statistics on the ages of those being enumerated are often in error, especially when the individual in question is not the respondent, such as when the head of the household fills in the census form on behalf of the entire family. If all ages were reported accurately, the size of each age group could be predicted based on the documented mortality for the population and the size of the birth cohort for that age group. However, evidence suggests that ages ending in 0 and 5 are actually over-reported, and ages ending in most odd digits, especially one, are under-reported.

If there were no mortality, the extent of digit preference in age reporting could be ascertained simply by comparing the total census counts for each digit of the reported age from 0 to 9. Because of mortality, however, there should be a decline in the expected count as one moves through the digits.

The following example will clarify the concepts of the previous paragraph. Suppose a population's age distribution on a particular census day is defined by the function $L_x = 1000(105-x)$, for $0 \leq x \leq 105$, where L_x is the number of people in the population who are age x last birthday. Table 1.2 shows the actual populations for ages 30 through 59.

TABLE 1.2

Age	Population	Age	Population	Age	Population	Total by Ending Digit
30	75,000	40	65,000	50	55,000	195,000
31	74,000	41	64,000	51	54,000	192,000
32	73,000	42	63,000	52	53,000	189,000
33	72,000	43	62,000	53	52,000	186,000
34	71,000	44	61,000	54	51,000	183,000
35	70,000	45	60,000	55	50,000	180,000
36	69,000	46	59,000	56	49,000	177,000
37	68,000	47	58,000	57	48,000	174,000
38	67,000	48	57,000	58	47,000	171,000
39	66,000	49	56,000	59	46,000	168,000

If the census were completely accurate (*i.e.*, if there were no digit preference in the age reporting), then the total responses by ending digit would be the values shown in the last column of Table 1.2.

Suppose this population has had a constant number of annual births for many years, no migration, and *no mortality*. Then the number alive on this census day would be the same at all ages, and therefore the total population at each ending digit would be the same for all ten ending digits. The presence of mortality, however, has produced the natural decreasing pattern in the column of total population by ending digit *even if* there is no digit preference in the reporting of ages. As a result, if there *were* digit preference, the effect of morality would make it hard for a demographer to detect such preference.

A method to counteract the effect of mortality, and thereby to ascertain if there is digit preference, is the *method of blending* proposed by Myers. (See Myers [21].) The Myers blending technique usually works best at a mid-range of ages, such as ages 20 to 79, where, due to mortality, the decline in population is approximately linear, as is the case for the population illustrated in

Table 1.2. (In the exercises the blending method is applied to other age groups.)

Let P_x denote the *reported* population at age x last birthday, as opposed to the *true* population at that age which we have denoted by L_x. To apply Myers' technique, a weighted average of the reported populations is calculated for each digit as

$$
\begin{aligned}
{}^b P_0 &= \tfrac{1}{10}P_{20} + P_{30} + \cdots + P_{60} + \tfrac{9}{10}P_{70} \\
{}^b P_1 &= \tfrac{2}{10}P_{21} + P_{31} + \cdots + P_{61} + \tfrac{8}{10}P_{71} \\
&\;\;\vdots \\
{}^b P_8 &= \tfrac{9}{10}P_{28} + P_{38} + \cdots + P_{68} + \tfrac{1}{10}P_{78} \\
{}^b P_9 &= \phantom{\tfrac{9}{10}}P_{29} + P_{39} + \cdots + P_{69} \; .
\end{aligned}
\tag{1.2}
$$

The factor $\dfrac{{}^b P_i}{\sum\limits_i {}^b P_i}$ is the proportion of responses ending in digit i in the blended population, and should be very close to $\tfrac{1}{10}$ if there is no digit preference. If these proportions are not $\tfrac{1}{10}$, then there is an indication of digit preference and the demographer may wish to reallocate responses to correct for the indicated errors.

To illustrate the technique numerically, consider the population illustrated in Table 1.2, and suppose there was no digit preference in age reporting so that $P_x = L_x$ for all x from age 30 through age 59. The blended populations would be as follows:

$$
\begin{aligned}
{}^b P_0 &= \tfrac{1}{10}P_{30} + P_{40} + \tfrac{9}{10}P_{50} &&= 122{,}000 \\
{}^b P_1 &= \tfrac{2}{10}P_{31} + P_{41} + \tfrac{8}{10}P_{51} &&= 122{,}000 \\
&\;\;\vdots \\
{}^b P_8 &= \tfrac{9}{10}P_{38} + P_{48} + \tfrac{1}{10}P_{58} &&= 122{,}000 \\
{}^b P_9 &= \phantom{\tfrac{9}{10}}P_{39} + P_{49} &&= 122{,}000
\end{aligned}
$$

Since ${}^b P_i$ is constant for $i = 0, 1, \ldots, 9$, it follows that the ratio $\dfrac{{}^b P_i}{\sum\limits_i {}^b P_i}$ is exactly $\tfrac{1}{10}$ for all i. It is the constancy of this ratio at $\tfrac{1}{10}$ that indicates the absence of digit preference. Conversely, if there *is* digit preference, then the ratios will deviate from $\frac{1}{10}$, and the demographer would normally reallocate the reported ages so as to obtain ratios closer to the constant $\frac{1}{10}$.

The crucial part in understanding the blending technique is to realize that the blending step is done to counteract the effects of mortality on the population. Without mortality, each reported ending digit total would itself be $\frac{1}{10}$ of the total reported population in absence of digit preference, so no blending would be required in order to check for digit preference. Because mortality is present, however, the blending step is required before the ratios are formed.

Another technique to reduce the effects of age misstatement is to form groups of responses, normally quinquennial. In this way, much of the error inherent in misstatement of age, or digit preference, cancels out. It is the grouped data that then become the basis of analysis.

In both Canada and the United States today, nearly all census data analysis starts with grouped data. Furthermore, the census forms now ask for year of birth, rather than age. Along with the higher levels of education existing today, these factors have eliminated the problem of digit preference, so no adjustments for it need be made.

1.4.4 Processing Errors

After census day the questionnaires are sent to regional processing sites. Nonwritten responses are usually in machine readable form. Written responses, such as name, must be separately coded. The coded information is then computerized either by keypunching or by electronic transferral. Mistakes can occur in coding or transmission, despite rigorous quality checks.

1.4.5 Sampling Errors

As previously noted, in both Canada and the United States all households receive the short-form questionnaire, but only a subset of the population receives the long-form questionnaire. The information collected from these households is weighted to produce estimates for the entire population. The simplest weighting procedure would be to multiply the results for the sample households by the sample ratio (five for many Canadian households and six for many U.S. households). This procedure is not used, however.

Sampling error can be reduced by using a complicated technique called *ratio estimation*. First, weights are derived from the ratio of complete-count short-form questionnaires to long-form samples within particular areas and population subgroups. Then instead of multiplying the sample responses by five (in Canada) or six (in the U.S.), the weights are adjusted so as to reproduce the total demographic characteristics for the area or subgroup revealed by the short-form questionnaires. For example, suppose in a particular area we know from the short form that there are 200 heads of household who have university degrees, but a one-in-five sampling reports only 36 rather than the expected 40. For this variable, all responses from the sample would be multiplied by $\frac{200}{36}$ rather than by 5 to estimate the total population response.

It is possible to present a mathematical statement of the variance associated with these sampling techniques. For example, the *standard error* of an estimate based on a sample of one in six households is

$$SE_X = \sqrt{5X\left(1 - \frac{X}{N}\right)} \, , \qquad (1.3)$$

where X is the estimated number of units with some characteristic and N is the total number of units in the area. (See Appendix A for a derivation and fuller explanation of Equation (1.3).) For example, if a one-in-six sample estimates that 247 persons ($X = 247$) in an area with 5021 inhabitants ($N = 5021$) have a certain characteristic, then the standard error is

$$SE_{247} = \sqrt{5 \times 247 \times \left(1 - \frac{247}{5021}\right)} = \sqrt{1174.25} = 34.3.$$

The corresponding formula for the standard error for estimated percentages is

$$SE_P = \sqrt{\frac{5P(100 - P)}{B}} \, , \qquad (1.4)$$

where P is the estimated percent and B is the base of the proportion, so that $.01P = \frac{X}{B}$. For example, the standard error of an estimate of 15 percent $(P=15)$ with a base of 1243 $(B=1243)$ can be computed as

$$SE_{.15} = \sqrt{\frac{5 \times 15 \times (100-15)}{1243}} = \sqrt{5.1} = 2.3,$$

measured in percentage points.

1.4.6 Gross Error Ratio/Net Error Ratio

Demographic data are subject to several sources of error, including errors of coverage, errors of content (or response errors), misstatement of age, processing errors, and sampling errors.

If data are published in grouped form, which is the norm, then it is possible for some errors to cancel. For example, someone may report their age incorrectly, but remain in the correct age group. Or a number of people may overstate a value while an equal number understate the same value.

This results in two measures of error, the *gross error ratio* and the *net error ratio.* The gross error ratio would measure the proportion of persons who are missclassified because of an error of content. The net error ratio is the net difference between the theoretically correct answer and the answer provided by the count, with the allowance of some errors being offset as described above. Net error ratios are usually much smaller than gross error ratios. It is also the case that both measures may only be estimates since it may not be possible to arrive at the absolutely correct answer.

To formulate this presentation, consider the following table.

| TABLE 1.3 |

Perfect Count	Reported Count		Total
	Number in Class	Number Not in Class	
Number in Class	a	b	$a+b$
Number Not in Class	c	d	$c+d$
Total	$a+c$	$b+d$	$n = a+b+c+d$

The reported count showed $a+c$ in the class, whereas the true or correct census should have been $a+b$. The net error ratio is given by $\frac{(a+b)-(a+c)}{n} = \frac{b-c}{n}$, usually expressed as a percentage. The total gross error, on the other hand, is represented by the sum $b+c$, so the gross error ratio is given by $\frac{b+c}{n}$, and is usually given as a percentage. The following example illustrates these concepts.

Suppose in a community of 1000 people, it is known that 20% are university graduates. Then $n = 1000$ and the number of people actually in this class is $a + b = 200$. Suppose the reported responses resulted in a net error ratio of -6% and a gross error ratio of $+14\%$. This tells us that $b + c = 140$ people responded incorrectly, either by saying they were graduates (although they actually were not) or by saying they were not (although they actually were). Similarly we see that $b - c = -60$ from the net error ratio, so we can now find $b = 40$, $c = 100$, $a = 160$, and $d = 700$. Thus we see that of the 200 university graduates, 160 confessed to it and 40 tried to hide it!

For census and vital registrations it is impossible to achieve a perfect result. However, there are several techniques in use that attempt to discover and correct errors in the data. We have already discussed methods used to reduce errors of coverage and content in the U.S. Census.

1.5 CONCLUSION

Census data quality information is disseminated in two ways. All census publications include a section on data quality that examines sources of errors and provides cautionary notes for users. In some cases, estimates of the magnitude of errors are given, such as estimates of sampling error. Information is also available in reports that summarize the results of data quality studies.

Other methods to determine and correct errors are limited only by the ingenuity of the demographer. For example, the update formula method, given by Equation (1.1), can be used to predict not only the total population, but any subcategory as well. For example, one group that is prone to census count errors is young males. Because this is a highly mobile group, they may be missed or double-counted in the census. By updating the age groups [5-10) and [10-15) from a previous census, the demographer can get an early estimate of the number to be expected among young males in the current census.

Similarly the demographer can look at sex ratios from adjacent age groups. Obviously, there should be a smooth and natural progression of sex ratios. The number of male births normally exceeds the number of female births. For example, in

Canada in 1986, 51.2% of births were male and 48.8% were female. At higher age groups, because of the higher mortality for males, this ratio will decline to 50/50 and beyond. The presence of age groups where the ratio produced by the census count is at odds with the projected ratio will indicate a possible source of error and will also provide the demographer with a possible correction factor.

The significance of error to the data user depends on the nature of the error, the intended use of the data, and the level of detail involved. As already stated, some errors occur more or less randomly and tend to cancel out when individual responses are aggregated for a sufficiently large group. For example, some people may overestimate their income while others underestimate. If there is no systemic tendency to error in either direction, then the errors will offset each other in any large aggregation. On the other hand, if many people forget a source of income, the result will be a general tendency to understate total income. In this case, the average reported income will be lower than the true average. Such *systemic* errors are far more serious a problem for most users than *random* errors. The bias they cause in the data persists no matter how large the group, and it is very difficult to measure.

Users of census and vital registration statistics must take the responsibility to determine the errors inherent in the data. Further, users must be sure to understand all the terms used in the presentation of the data. For example, does the term "income" refer to family income or individual income? What does the word "unemployed" actually mean? Users should take the care to review all definitions and source-of-error information carefully and to be aware of data limitations in any subsequent analysis.

1.6 EXERCISES

1.1 Introduction;   1.2 The Collection of Demographic Statistics

1-1. With respect to the taking of a census, (a) define and differentiate the *de facto* and *de jure* approaches, and (b) list their advantages and disadvantages.

1-2. Define and give examples of vital statistics. At which political level are vital statistics collected in Canada and the United States?

1-3. Define population register and list its advantages and disadvantages.

1.3 Taking the Census

1-4. Outline the sampling techniques used in taking the 1986 Canadian census and the 1990 United States census.

1.4 Sources of Errors and Their Corrections

1-5. With respect to census-taking, define and differentiate the following items.

(a) Coverage errors   (c) Processing errors
(b) Content errors   (d) Sampling errors

1-6. How are coverage and content errors addressed?

1-7. In a region with 50,000 inhabitants, one-in-six sampling was used to estimate the number of inhabitants owning BMWs. If the unadjusted standard error of estimate was 17.31011, how many reported owning a BMW?

1-8. Define and differentiate between allocations and substitutions.

1-9. A small country has three provinces. A *de facto* census shows population counts of 45,000 for Province X, 25,500 for Province Y, and 64,500 for Province Z.

A post-census survey indicated that on census day, (i) 5% of Province X residents were in Province Y and 10% were in Province Z, (ii) 10% of Province Y residents were in Province X and 10% were in Province Z, (iii) 0% of Province Z residents were in Province X and 5% were in Province Y. What would a *de jure* census find?

1-10. Consider the following data for Australia from 1954 to 1961.

Population June 30, 1954 (census)   8,986,530
During period 1954-61
    Births   1,544,240
    Deaths   600,551
    Immigrants   1,766,858
    Emigrants   1,182,104
Population June 30, 1961 (census) 10,508,186

Determine the error of closure.

1-11. For a census, the ratio of the blended population at each ending digit (using Myers' technique) to the total blended population are given as follows.

Ending Digit	Ratio
0	.11
1	.12
2	.13
3	.11
4	.10
5	.07
6	.08
7	.07
8	.09
9	.12

As the first step in the graduation process, the demographer plans to group the data into quinquennial age groupings that will minimize the effect of digit preferences. What is the best quinquennial grouping?

1-12. In a certain community of 1000 persons, 460 were reported as having a certain characteristic. Upon re-enumeration it was discovered that really only 400 persons had this characteristic. Find the net error ratio. Can the gross error ratio be calculated?

1-13. You are given the following population data (in thousands) about males in England and Wales in 1911.

Digit of Age	Population Starting at	
x	Age 10+x	Age 20+x
0	1,638.8	1,279.7
1	1,402.2	1,050.9
2	1,461.8	1,112.6
3	1,373.0	1,027.9
4	1,367.9	1,025.0
5	1,350.1	1,015.8
6	1,320.9	985.4
7	1,234.9	905.3
8	1,297.6	965.0
9	1,215.1	892.2

Each totaled population in the table represents the sum of nine reported populations. For example, for digit 0 the population $10+x$ covers ages 10 through 90 and the population $20+x$ covers ages 20 to 100. Find the percentage of the blended population (using Myers' technique) reporting digit 3.

1-14. Given the following information, what quinquennial data grouping would best overcome the indicated digit preference?

Digit of Age	Myers Blended Population	Ratio to Digit 9
0	1,315,600	1.083
1	1,121,200	.923
2	1,217,400	1.002
3	1,165,900	.960
4	1,196,400	.985
5	1,216,400	1.001
6	1,220,200	1.004
7	1,169,000	.962
8	1,264,300	1.041
9	1,215,100	1.000

1-15. You are given the following data for males in the 1970 census of West Malaysia.

Terminal Digit	Sum of Population by Single Year of Age	
	Age Group 35-54	Age Group 45-64
5	77,646	57,354
6	77,698	65,010
7	68,370	53,108
8	52,033	33,346
9	50,569	32,608
0	81,668	52,654
1	80,269	69,972
2	68,157	57,121
3	61,828	43,379
4	64,415	45,879

Based on Myers' method, which terminal digit is most over-reported and which is most underreported? (Note that Myers' technique must be modified to start at digit 5, rather than digit 0.)

1-16. Consider the following information:
Actual population on January 1, 1980: 100,000

	Number of Occurrences Recorded Between	
	1/1/80 and 1/1/81	1/1/80 and 1/1/90
Births	1,500	18,000
Deaths	850	10,000
Net Immigration	350	6,500

The recorded occurrences between 1/1/80 and 1/1/81 were used to model the expected population change from 1/1/80 to 1/1/90. Only then did the true statistics become available. Determine (a) the linearly projected 1/1/90 population, (b) the actual 1/1/90 population, and (c) the error of closure.

CHAPTER 2

MEASURES OF MORTALITY AND FERTILITY

2.1 INTRODUCTION

Demographers use a number of statistics in their analysis of population dynamics. These statistics should be carefully understood and used consistently. Unfortunately some statistics that are commonly used with colloquial acceptance are technically used incorrectly. For example, the net error ratio defined in Chapter 1 is improperly called the net error rate in various publications.

Confusion can exist among terms such as ratios, proportions, and rates.

Any two measures can be compared in the form of a *ratio*. For example, assume that for every 100 births, 52 are male and 48 are female. The ratio of male to female births is 52 to 48, or 52/48. We could also state that the ratio of female to male births is 48 to 52.

If the denominator of the comparative statistic is the total number of all possible occurrences, then we have a *proportion*. For example, the proportion of male births out of total births is 52/100 and the proportion of female births is 48/100.

If the proportion is quoted as a measure per hundred, it is referred to as a *percent*. Hence the male birth proportion is 52% and the female birth proportion is 48%.

If the statistic is associated with a time interval, it can be quoted as a *rate*. For example, if there are 100 births in a year, in a country with a midyear population of 7000, then the annual birth rate is 14.3 per 1000.

Unfortunately many statistics commonly referred to as rates are not. For example, if 60% of the female population of a certain age group is in the labor force, this statistic is often referred to as the female labor force participation rate. In fact, this is a proportion and not a rate. Similarly, the percentage of the population that is out of work and actively looking for work on a particular day is normally called the unemployment rate. This is, in fact, the unemployment proportion.

In this text, the colloquially accepted phrase will be adopted. Readers should be aware that if a technically incorrect phrase has become widely accepted, it will be found in publications that are otherwise meticulously accurate.

2.2 CRUDE RATES

Crude rates are normally defined as the ratio of the number of vital events which occurred in a defined population in one calendar year, to the size of the population at midyear. The midyear statistic is used to approximate the average size of the population over the year.

For example, in the United States in 1986 there was a total of 2.1 million deaths and a midyear population of 241.6 million. Then the *crude death rate* for 1986 is defined to be $\frac{2.1}{241.6} = .00869$, which is frequently expressed as 8.69 per 1000. In general we will express the crude death rate for calendar year z as

$$d_c^z = \frac{D^z}{P(z)}, \tag{2.1}$$

where D^z is the number of deaths in calendar year z and $P(z)$ is the midyear population.

Similarly, the *crude birth rate* for calendar year z is defined as

$$b_c^z = \frac{B^z}{P(z)}, \tag{2.2}$$

where B^z denotes the number of live births in calendar year z. For example, there were 3.7 million live births in the United States in 1986, so the crude birth rate for that year was $\frac{3.7}{241.6} = .01531$, or 15.31 per 1000.

A word about notation is in order. In this text we will use symbols such as B^z and D^z to denote measures taken *over* a calendar year, and symbols such as $P(z)$ to denote measures taken at a *point of time* within a calendar year. Although $P(z)$ normally is used as the *midyear* population, it actually arises from the census count which is taken on April 1 in the United States. This use of a census count as an approximation to the midyear population is very common in demographic analysis.

Another crude measure is the *crude rate of natural increase*, defined as the crude birth rate less the crude death rate. Notationally we have

$$r_c^z = b_c^z - d_c^z. \tag{2.3}$$

The crude rate of natural increase gives a rough measure of the internal (*i.e.*, without migration) rate of growth of a population.

In a similar fashion we can define a wide variety of crude rates such as *crude marriage rates*, *crude divorce rates*, *crude immigration rates*, and so on. Crude rates should be used with care, if not outright skepticism, for reasons that will be presented in the following sections.

Example 2.1

Given the following data, determine (a) the proportion of deaths that are male, (b) the percentage of deaths that are female, (c) the ratio of female to male deaths, and (d) the crude death rate.

Midyear	Deaths in Calendar Year z		
Population	Male	Female	Total
20.1 million	77,330	42,192	119,522

Solution

(a) Proportion (male) $\dfrac{77,330}{119,522} = .647$

(b) Percentage (female) $\dfrac{42,192}{119,522} = 35.3\%$

(c) Ratio (f/m) $\dfrac{42,192}{77,330} = .546$

(d) Crude death rate (d_c^z) $\dfrac{119,522}{20,100,000} = .00595$ □

2.3 AGE-SPECIFIC MORTALITY RATES

Table 2.1 below provides data on age-specific mortality rates, denoted $_nm_x$, for the states of Michigan and Florida. Each age-specific rate is calculated as a crude rate would be, dividing deaths by midyear population, except that only deaths and population between ages x and $x+n$ are considered. The total number of deaths for the state of Michigan in 1985 was 78,712 and the total population July 1, 1985 was 9,087,000, giving an overall crude death rate of 8.66 per 1000. Similarly, the total number of deaths for Florida was 121,075 and its total population was 11,368,000, for a crude death rate of 10.65 per 1000.

These crude death rates are surprisingly different (a 23% difference) if we compare the age-specific rates as listed. The reason for this wide variation is the significant difference in the underlying demographics of the two states, as seen in Table 2.1 on the following page.

Obviously the crude death rate in Florida may not be indicative of a higher mortality profile, but may only indicate that more elderly people live in Florida than live in Michigan. Therefore, to compare the mortality profiles of two jurisdictions, we are well advised not to use their crude death rates. Section 2.4 provides two more accurate methods for comparing mortality rates between areas.

2.4 ADJUSTED MEASURES OF MORTALITY

Depending on the data available to the demographer, there are two standard methods of arriving at statistics that more fairly compare the level of mortality in two jurisdictions.

The more accurate of the two methods is called the *direct method of adjustment*, and can be used only if age-specific mortality rates are available for the two jurisdictions. When this is the case, a standard population is then chosen. In the above example, a natural choice for the standard population would be the U.S. population in 1985, presented in Table 2.2 on page 26.

We then apply the age-specific (and perhaps also sex-specific) mortality rates of jurisdiction j to the standard population, to arrive at the death rate in the standard population if it were to experience the age-specific (sex-specific) mortality of jurisdiction j. Algebraically the adjusted death rate by the direct

TABLE 2.1a

MICHIGAN				
Age Group	Population on July 1, 1985 (thousands)	Percent	Deaths in 1985	$_n m_x \cdot 10^3$
0-5	662	7.3	1,889	2.85
5-15	1,366	15.0	385	0.28
15-25	1,568	17.3	1,543	0.98
25-35	1,600	17.6	2,049	1.28
35-45	1,186	13.1	2,592	2.19
45-55	842	9.3	4,512	5.36
55-65	844	9.3	11,460	13.58
65-75	618	6.8	18,264	29.55
75-85	306	3.4	20,637	67.44
85+	95	1.0	15,381	161.91
Total	9,087		78,712	8.66

TABLE 2.1b

FLORIDA				
Age Group	Population on July 1, 1985 (thousands)	Percent	Deaths in 1985	$_n m_x \cdot 10^3$
0-5	750	6.6	2,241	2.99
5-15	1,348	11.9	419	0.31
15-25	1,677	14.8	1,847	1.10
25-35	1,775	15.6	2,713	1.53
35-45	1,402	12.3	3,270	2.33
45-55	1,105	9.7	5,986	5.42
55-65	1,308	11.5	15,301	11.70
65-75	1,201	10.6	29,875	24.88
75-85	641	5.6	36,292	56.62
85+	161	1.4	23,131	143.67
Total	11,368		121,075	10.65

method of adjustment is given by

$$ADR_D = \frac{\sum_x {}_nP_x^s \cdot {}_nm_x^j}{\sum_x {}_nP_x^s} = \frac{\sum_x {}_nP_x^s \cdot {}_nm_x^j}{P^s}, \qquad (2.4)$$

where ${}_nP_x^s$ is the standard population aged x to $x+n$, and ${}_nm_x^j$ is the age-specific mortality rate for jurisdiction j.

TABLE 2.2

UNITED STATES				
Age Group	Population on July 1, 1985 (thousands)	Percent	Deaths in 1985	${}_nm_x \cdot 10^3$
0-5	18,004	7.54	47,369	2.63
5-15	33,923	14.21	8,933	0.26
15-25	39,551	16.57	37,935	0.96
25-35	42,027	17.60	51,852	1.23
35-45	31,764	13.31	65,815	2.07
45-55	22,589	9.46	116,634	5.16
55-65	22,337	9.36	286,480	12.83
65-75	17,009	7.12	482,646	28.38
75-85	8,836	3.70	568,848	64.38
85+	2,695	1.13	419,051	155.49
Total	238,735		2,086,440*	8.74

*Age not stated for 877 deaths.

Using the state data for Michigan and Florida given in Table 2.1, we find the adjusted death rate is 9.1413 for Michigan and 8.1281 for Florida, by the direct method of adjustment. These statistics are not subject to distortions caused by the different underlying demographics of the two states, as was true for the crude death rate. Therefore, we can now state that, overall, Florida has a slightly preferable mortality profile than Michigan.

Sometimes age-specific mortality rates for jurisdiction j are not available. In such cases, demographers revert to the less-favored *indirect method of adjustment.*

Again, start by choosing a standard population for which age-specific mortality rates are available. Then calculate the expected number of deaths in jurisdiction j, if it were to experience the mortality of the standard population, which is given by

$$\sum_x {}_n m_x^s \cdot {}_n P_x^j. \tag{2.5}$$

Then compare the actual total deaths in jurisdiction j to the expected deaths calculated by (2.5), to arrive at a statistic called the *standardized mortality ratio* (*SMR*), given by

$$SMR = \frac{D^j}{\sum_x {}_n m_x^s \cdot {}_n P_x^j}. \tag{2.6}$$

Finally, multiply the standardized mortality ratio by the crude death rate for the standard population to get the adjusted death rate by the indirect method, given by

$$ADR_I = \frac{D^j}{\sum_x {}_n m_x^s \cdot {}_n P_x^j} \cdot \frac{D^s}{P^s}. \tag{2.7}$$

(In other texts ADR_I is called the *standardized mortality rate*.) In the example above, the standardized mortality ratio for Michigan is 1.0465 and for Florida is .9180. The crude death rate for the United States is 8.7396, so the adjusted death rate by the indirect method is 9.1457 for Michigan and 8.0227 for Florida.

It should noted that mortality rates can be adjusted with respect to variables other than age, as illustrated in Exercise 2-7.

2.5 MEASURES OF INFANT MORTALITY

Special efforts are made to determine the death rate at age 0, and rates for subsets of the first year of life, such as the first day of life, the first week of life, and so on. The methods specifically used in Canada and the United States are outlined in Chapter 4.

The extra care taken with the evaluation of the mortality rate in the first year of life is partly because the value is large (not exceeded until after age 55 in most societies), changes rapidly by age (*e.g.*, age 0-1 day, versus age 1-12 months), and is often used as a single statistic to measure the general level of health for an entire country or demographic subset, such as native people. In fact, given only the infant mortality rate, a demographer can predict with a fair degree of accuracy the mortality profile at all ages for a given population, using pre-existing United Nations Model Life Tables.

To be consistent with the approach of Section 2.3, we could have defined the infant crude death rate for calendar year z to be

$$\frac{D_0^z}{P_0(z)}, \tag{2.8}$$

where D_0^z is the number of deaths under age 1 during calendar year z and $P_0(z)$ is the estimated midyear population under age 1.

However, because of high infant mortality and a degree of seasonality in the pattern of births, and because accurate estimates of $P_0(z)$ are only available in census years, the measure defined by (2.8) is, in fact, not used. Instead, demographers calculate a crude infant mortality rate as

$$\frac{D_0^z}{B^z}, \tag{2.9}$$

where B^z is the number of live births in calendar year z.

This crude infant mortality rate is not an ideal measure of infant mortality, since the correct population exposed to the risk of death (*i.e.*, the population from which the observed deaths arose) includes some infants born in the previous calendar year. When the number of births, B^z, does not change appreciably from one calendar year to the next, (2.9) will produce satisfactory results. In cases where B^z does change rapidly, then some adjustments to (2.9) are required. The goal is to allocate the infant deaths to their correct year of birth and relate them to the corresponding number of births exposed to risk. This leads to an *adjusted infant mortality rate*, given by

$$\left[\frac{D_0^z(1-\rho_0^z)}{B^z} + \frac{D_0^z \, \rho_0^z}{B^{z-1}} \right], \tag{2.10}$$

where ρ_0^z is the proportion of infant deaths in year z for which the year of birth was year $z-1$. Details of how this adjusted infant mortality rate is actually derived in Canada and the United States are discussed in Chapter 4.

Because early infant deaths are usually associated with birth defects of prematurity (endogenous factors), whereas later deaths in the first year of life are usually associated with external (exogenous) factors such as disease and accidents, the infant mortality statistics are often split and analyzed separately. They are analyzed as to those that occur in the first 28 days of life (*neonatal* deaths) and those that occur thereafter (*post-neonatal* deaths). Hence the *neonatal mortality rate* is computed in the same way as the conventional infant mortality rate, except that the deaths (numerator) are those occurring in the first 28 days of life.

Neonatal deaths combined with stillbirths of gestation beyond 28 weeks are referred to as *perinatal* mortality. This statistic may be used as an alternative measure of the general health of a population.

Infant mortality has declined rapidly in most nations in this century. However, the wide variation in infant mortality rates from country to country and between differing demographic strata (*e.g.*, the poor versus the wealthy) show that much more improvement can still be achieved.

2.6 AGE-SPECIFIC FERTILITY RATES

The crude birth rate, which can also be viewed as a *crude fertility rate*, was defined earlier as the total number of live births in a calendar year divided by the midyear population. As was true for mortality rates, it is more meaningful and useful to develop fertility rates that are specific for the age of the mother. Thus we define the *age-specific fertility rate* for calendar year z as

$$f_x^z = \frac{B^z}{F_x(z)}, \qquad (2.11a)$$

where $F_x(z)$ is the estimated midyear female population at age x last birthday. More generally,

$$_n f_x^z = \frac{B^z}{_n F_x(z)}, \qquad (2.11b)$$

where $_n F_x(z)$ is the estimated midyear female population between ages x and $x+n$. The Canadian age-specific fertility rates for 1986 using quinquennial age groups (*i.e.*, $n=5$) are shown in Table 2.3.

TABLE 2.3

Canadian Data, 1986			
Age	Midyear Female Population	Number of Live Births in 1986	Age-specific Fertility Rates
(1)	(2)	(3)	(4)
10-15	870,050	210	.000241
15-20	939,600	21,452	.022832
20-25	1,121,895	92,915	.082820
25-30	1,176,520	143,563	.122023
30-35	1,101,880	81,431	.073902
35-40	1,015,120	22,419	.022085
40-45	803,785	2,538	.003158
45-50	655,915	86	.000131
			.327190×5 = 1.635950

A statistic called the *total fertility rate* (TFR) for calendar year z is obtained by adding together the age-specific fertility rates for each age. Thus we have

$$TFR^z = \sum_{x=\alpha}^{\beta} f_x^z, \qquad (2.12)$$

where α and β are the lower and upper limits of the child-bearing ages. However, since Table 2.3 uses 5-year age groups, we must multiply the total of the age-specific rates by five to arrive at the TFR, which is 1.636 in this case. This statistic measures the number of children born to the average female if she follows the birthing pattern being experienced today by the overall population. It is often presented as a rate per 1000 females, which is 1636 in this case.

If the TFR is calculated in calendar year z, as suggested by Equation (2.12), the births used in the calculation are from mothers with birth years between year $z-10$ and year $z-49$. Therefore, this TFR is not a measure of the fertility of a particular cohort or generation, but rather it is a statistic that measures the rate of birthing at a point in time. To measure the fertility rate of a generation born in year z we would have to wait until year $z+49$, when the entire cohort reaches the end of its period of *fecundity*, the physiological ability to bear children. The timeliness of the TFR calculated by the calendar year method, which we have denoted TFR^z, makes it a more valuable statistic than if it were calculated by the generation method.

The total fertility rate is a clearer measure of the reproductivity index of a population than the crude birth rate of Section 2.2, because the TFR is independent of the age distribution of the population. For example, as the Baby Boom generation in Canada and the United States (which was born between approximately 1951 and 1966) passes through its period of fecundity in the 1990's, it is quite possible that the total fertility rate in both countries could continue to fall, although at the same time the crude birth rate could stay constant or even rise. In this case the total fertility rate is a superior measure of the population's reproductivity.

As can be seen in Figure 2.1 on the following page, the total fertility rate in Canada at the present time is close to 1.65, and the U.S. equivalent is close to 1.92. Obviously, were these rates to continue in the long run without immigration, both populations would be in a state of decline. These fertility rates do not provide a replacement ratio high enough to equal zero population growth. In fact, it would take a total fertility rate of approximately 2.1 to achieve a zero population growth rate. The rate is in excess of 2.0 to allow for mortality between birth and the end of the period of reproduction.

With respect to Figure 2.1, several comments are relevant. First, had one been employed as a demographer in the late 1930's, with the assignment of projecting the expected total fertility rate for the 1980's, it is likely that, using some basic mathematical modelling, one would have come very close to the total fertility rates actually experienced. The only problem is that one would have been completely wrong for the entire intervening period! The unexpected rise and fall of the total fertility rate that has become known as the Postwar Baby Boom / Baby Bust, and its implications, will be explored in more depth in Chapter 8.

The most important variable in any population projection, and the most difficult to predict, is the total fertility rate. There are two popular theories on where fertility rates might go in the future. These two theories lead to widely different outcomes.

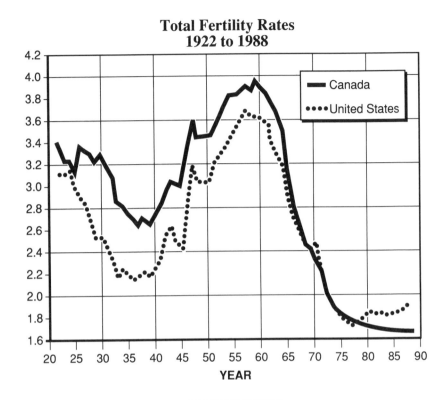

**Total Fertility Rates
1922 to 1988**

Source: [25] and [28]

FIGURE 2.1

Easterlin [8] has postulated that fertility rates rise and fall in a wavelike pattern with a cycle length, from peak to peak or from trough to trough, of two generations. He points out that couples from a small cohort, such as those born in the 1930's, will find life relatively easy. Jobs are plentiful, advancement is fast, and wealth is accumulated more easily than anticipated. Such couples will tend to have large families, as they did.

On the other hand, couples from a large cohort, such as those born in the 1950's and 1960's, will find life more difficult. Unemployment is high, advancement is slow, and wealth is more difficult to accumulate. These couples will tend to have small families. If Easterlin is correct, then one might expect the next Baby Boom to begin sometime in the 1990's.

The British demographer Ermisch [9] starts from the same basis, since he has to explain the Baby Boom of the 1950/60's, but comes to a different conclusion. He says that in a one-earner family, if the worker's real wages rise rapidly and the cost of children remains constant, that family will have more children. This is what happened in the 1950/60's. In a two-earner family, however, if real wages rise rapidly, but the wife has to leave the work force or interrupt a career path to bear and raise children, then the cost of children rises and fertility rates will not change. Ermisch's data show that the higher a woman's earning power, the longer the gap between marriage and first birth. He also points out that the increased probability of divorce may keep the fertility rate down. In conclusion, Ermisch sees no reason to believe that fertility rates will rise at all. He anticipates that they will now level off at about their present level, which is below replacement rate. His theory could be used to justify the constant future fertility assumption underlying the projections referred to in Chapter 8.

The total fertility rate in Canada has been more variable than in the United States, and the impact of this variability will be discussed in Chapter 8. It reinforces how difficult it is to project fertility rates with any level of confidence.

Age-specific fertility rates can also be specific for the sex of the birth. For example, the general female *age-and-sex-specific fertility rate* for calendar year z is defined as

$$_n f_x^{f,z} \ = \ \frac{B^{f,z}}{_n F_x(z)}, \tag{2.13a}$$

where $B^{f,z}$ denotes the female live births in calendar year z to mothers between ages x and $x+n$. The corresponding male rate would be defined as

$$_n f_x^{m,z} \ = \ \frac{B^{m,z}}{_n M_x(z)}, \tag{2.13b}$$

where $B^{m,z}$ denotes the male live births in calendar year z to fathers between ages x and $x+n$, and $_n M_x(z)$ denotes the midyear male population. If the midyear populations are available by each year of age, then we would use $F_x(z)$ and $M_x(z)$ in the denomin-

ators of (2.13a) and (2.13b), respectively, and the resulting age-
and-sex-specific fertility rates would be denoted by $f_x^{f,z}$ and $f_x^{m,z}$,
respectively. Note, however, that the male rates are seldom produced, because it is difficult to obtain accurate information regarding the ages of the fathers of the male births.

The total of the female age-and-sex-specific fertility rates is
called the *gross reproduction rate* (GRR) for calendar year z. Thus
we have

$$GRR^z = \sum_{x=\alpha}^{\beta} f_x^{f,z}. \tag{2.14}$$

As we saw in the case of TFR^z, if we are summing values of $_nf_x^{f,z}$,
then the total must be multiplied by n to obtain the GRR. It
should be clear that the GRR is approximately one-half of the
TFR.

The *net reproduction rate* (NRR) further accounts for mortality between the birth of the daughter and the age of the mother.
It is defined as

$$NRR^z = \sum_{x=\alpha}^{\beta} f_x^{f,z} \cdot {}_xp_0^f, \tag{2.15}$$

where $_xp_0^f$ denotes the probability that a newborn female will
survive to age x. If values of $_nf_x^{f,z}$ are used, then the appropriate
probability to use is one that measures survival to the middle of
the age group of the mother, which is age $x+\frac{1}{2}n$. (See Chapter 3 for
a fuller development of the survival probability concept.)

The calculation of the GRR and the NRR for Canada in
1986 is illustrated in Table 2.4 on the following page. The net
reproduction rate of .785410 indicates that this cohort of females is
not expected to replace itself. If this level of fertility and mortality
were to continue, without net immigration the Canadian population would ultimately decline in size.

In general, the population will either grow, reach a stationary level (see Chapter 5), or decline, depending on whether the
NRR is greater than, equal to, or less than unity.

The net reproduction rate is a measure of the internal rate
of growth of a population without migration. This description was
also given to the crude rate of natural increase, which is the crude
birth rate less the crude death rate, and is usually in the range of

−1% to +3% (see Figure 2.2 on page 36). Some further discussion of these two measurements will be useful.

In 1986 the net reproduction rate was NRR^{86} = .785 in Canada. The crude birth rate was b_c^{86} = .0147 and the crude death rate was d_c^{86} = .0073, for a crude rate of natural increase of .0074, or 7.4 per 1000. The NRR value shows that ultimately the Canadian population will decline if there is no migration. However, given the present age mix of the population, it is growing at an overall rate of .74%, due to the "momentum" created by the Baby Boomers and their children. Any actual decline in the Canadian population, as suggested by the NRR, will not occur until well into the next century.

TABLE 2.4

Age Group	Females Born to Mothers in Each Group	Midyear Female Population in Each Group	Age-specific Female Fertility Rates	Probability of Female Surviving to Middle of Age Group of Mother	Fertility Rate Times Survival Probability
(1)	(2)	(3)	(4)	(5)	(6)
10-15	101	870,050	.000116	.99043	.000115
15-20	10,362	939,600	.011028	.98897	.010906
20-25	45,412	1,121,895	.040478	.98691	.039948
25-30	70,021	1,176,520	.059515	.98486	.058613
30-35	39,844	1,101,880	.036160	.98240	.035523
35-40	10,812	1,015,120	.010651	.97907	.010428
40-45	1,225	803,785	.001524	.97381	.001484
45-50	44	655,915	.000067	.96496	.000065
Total			.159539		.157082
(Times 5 for quinquennial intervals)			.797695		.785410
Gross reproduction rate: .797695					
Net reproduction rate: .785410					

Note that the totals in Columns (4) and (6) are multiplied by 5 to obtain the GRR and NRR, respectively. If single-age data were used, each fertility rate in Column (4) would be of the same order of magnitude as are the five-year average rates shown, but

there would be five times as many of them. Thus, when quinquennial data is used, the column totals are multiplied by 5.

Further analysis of population growth rates will be explored
when we examine stable population theory in Chapter 6.

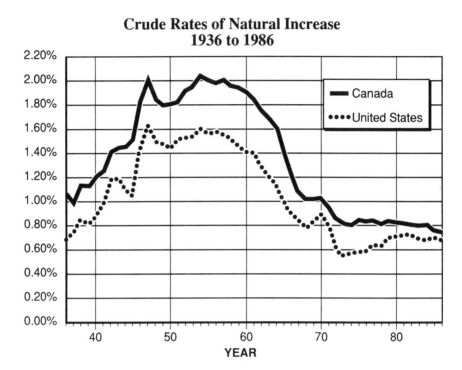

FIGURE 2.2

Source: [25] and [28]

2.7 EXERCISES

2.1 Introduction;   2.2 Crude Rates

2-1. A population closed to migration and increasing in a linear fashion is enumerated every January 1. These censuses are completely accurate. Population *estimates* based on the country's vital registration system, however, are subject to error. The census of 1987 produced a count of 1,000. An estimate of 1,260 for January 1, 1988 was found to be subject, after the 1988 census was conducted, to an error of closure of -5%. Based on census enumerations, determine the crude rate of natural increase during calendar year 1987.

2-2. Consider a population on July 1, 1980 equal to 1,000,000 and growing at 2% per year as a continuous instantaneous rate. The crude rate of natural increase for 1990 was 3% and the crude rate of death was 1%. Determine the number of live births in 1990.

2.3 Age-Specific Mortality Rates;
2.4 Adjusted Measures of Mortality

2-3 Consider the following data for a community and a standard population.

	Community			Standard Population		
Age	No. Alive July 1, z	Deaths in z	$_n m_x^z$	No. Alive July 1, z	Deaths in z	$_n m_x^z$
0-20	5,000	25	.005	700,000	700	.001
20-40	3,000	18	.006	500,000	1,000	.002
40-60	2,000	20	.010	400,000	1,600	.004
60-80	1,000	20	.020	100,000	1,000	.010
	11,000	83		1,700,000	4,300	

(a) Calculate the crude death rate for the community.
(b) Calculate the directly adjusted death rate.
(c) Calculate the indirectly adjusted death rate.

2-4.   Consider the following information.

	Country A		State X	
Age	Census Population	Deaths	Census Population	Deaths
0-20	100,000	1,000	10,000	200
20-40	80,000	1,600	9,000	90
40-60	60,000	1,800	7,000	280
60-80	40,000	2,000	3,000	150
80+	20,000	2,000	1,000	150

Using the Country A data as the standard population, calculate the indirectly adjusted death rate for State X.

2-5.   Consider the following data.

Age	Total Population		Subpopulation One		Subpopulation Two	
	Midyear	Deaths	Midyear	Deaths	Midyear	Deaths
0-20	10,000	1,000	1,000	800	1,000	
20-30	100,000	2,000	10,000	1,000	10,000	
30-40	1,000,000	3,000	10,000	2,000	10,000	
40-50	1,000,000	50,000	10,000	2,000	10,000	
50+	1,000,000	100,000	1,000	500	1,000	
Total	3,110,000	156,000	32,000	6,300	32,000	2,000

Calculate the absolute difference in the adjusted mortality rates for Subpopulations One and Two.   Use the best method of adjustment for each population.

2-6.   Treatments A and B were applied to two populations with the following results.

	Number Showing Improvement	
	A	B
Females	100 of 1000	0 of 500
Males	500 of 500	700 of 1000
Total	600 of 1500	700 of 1500

Which treatment is better?   Explain.

2-7. The following perinatal mortality data for 1985 were published in a recent government report.

Geographic Area/Race	Number of Perinatal Deaths	Perinatal Mortality Rate
Metropolitan Counties	31,075	.0107
White Race	21,456	.0095
All Other Races	9,619	.0151
Nonmetropolitan Counties	9,485	.0108
White Race	7,307	.0099
All Other Races	2,178	.0158

Using metropolitan counties as the standard, calculate the
perinatal mortality rate directly adjusted with respect to *race*
for nonmetropolitan counties.

2-8. For a certain calendar year, you are given the following
information.

(i)

Age Group	Midyear Population	
	Country X	Country Y
0-40	400,000	800,000
40+	200,000	300,000
Total	600,000	1,100,000

(ii) Death rates for the age group 0-40 were the same for
both countries.
(iii) The crude death rate for Country X was 10 per 1000
persons.
(iv) The directly adjusted death rate for Country Y was 12
per 1000 persons, based on the given data and Country X
as the standard.

Determine the absolute difference between the death rates
for Country X and Country Y for the age group 40 and over.

2-9.   You are given the following information.

Age	Country X Population (mid-1985)	Country X Deaths (during 1985)	Country Y Population (mid-1985)
0-5	16,700,000	55,000	80,000
5-15	35,200,000	10,000	150,000
15-25	43,100,000	50,000	180,000
25-45	64,400,000	110,000	200,000
45-65	45,200,000	420,000	120,000
65+	25,400,000	1,300,000	80,000
Total	230,000,000	1,945,000	810,000

Using Country X as the standard, the indirectly adjusted death rate for Country Y in 1985 is 14.27 per 1000 persons. Calculate the actual number of deaths in Country Y during 1985.

2-10. You are given the following facts about Country Y for 1980.

(i)   The number of live births was 500,000.
(ii) The total number of deaths was 100,000.
(iii) The crude birth rate was 40 per 1000.

Assume that Country Y was used as the standard population. The standardized mortality ratio for Community X in 1980 was 1.25. Determine the indirectly adjusted death rate for Community X during 1980.

2.5 Measures of Infant Mortality

2-11. Given the following data, determine the adjusted and unadjusted infant mortality rates for 1990 if 70% of those who died at age 0 were born in the same calendar year that death occurred.

Infant Deaths 1989	Infant Deaths 1990	Births 1989	Births 1990
3500	3900	25,000	27,000

2-12. For a certain community you have the following information.

Age at Death	Number of Deaths in 1990
0-28 days	2600
29-365 days	1500

There were 22,000 births in 1990. Calculate the neonatal mortality rate and the infant mortality rate.

2-13. Using the following information, find ρ_0^{90}.

	1989	1990
Births	5237	7210
Deaths at age 0	210	280

The 1990 infant morality rate (adjusted) was .0432.

2-14. Consider the following information.

Number of live births	100,000
Number of stillbirths	800
Infant deaths in first week of life	600
Total Infant deaths in first 28 days of life	1000
Total Infant deaths in first year of life	2300

Determine (a) the perinatal mortality rate and (b) the neo-natal mortality rate

2-15. You are given the following information.

Period	Number of Deaths
Neonatal	27
Post-neonatal	13
Stillbirths	7

The number of live births is not given, but the perinatal rate is stated as 85 per 1000 live births. Determine the infant morality rate.

2.6 Age-Specific Fertility Rates

2-16. Which of the following would indicate exactly zero population growth, so that ultimately, without migration, a population of constant size would result?

(a) $TFR = 2.0$ (c) $GRR = 1.0$
(b) $GRR = 2.0$ (d) $NRR = 1.0$

2-17. You are given the following data for Canada for 1986.

Age Group	Midyear Female Population	Number of Live Births to Mothers in Age Group			Probability of Survival to Middle of Age Group
		Male	Female	Total	
10-15	870,050	109	101	210	.99051
15-20	939,600	11,090	10,362	21,452	.98917
20-25	1,121,895	47,503	45,412	92,915	.98711
25-30	1,176,520	73,542	70,021	143,563	.98507
30-35	1,101,880	41,587	39,844	81,431	.98268
35-40	1,015,120	11,607	10,812	22,419	.97947
40-45	803,785	1,313	1,225	2,538	.97449
45-50	655,915	42	44	86	.96608

(a) Find the total fertility rate.
(b) Find the gross reproduction rate.
(c) Find the net reproduction rate.

2-18. The following information is given for a certain species of cat.

Age Last Birthday	Age-Specific Fertility Rate (Female to Female)	Probability of Surviving to Age of Mother
0	0	.850
1	2.0	.665
2	3.0	.567
3	1.5	.358
4	0	.101

(a)   Calculate the gross reproduction rate.
(b)   Calculate the net reproduction rate.

2-19. You are given the following data for a population of animals for 1988. No births occur before age 3 or after age 12.

Age Group	Female Births to Mothers in Each Age Group	Midyear Female Population in Each Age Group	Probability of Daughter Surviving from Birth to Middle of Age Group of Mother
3-6	5,000	100,000	.98
6-9	5,000	200,000	.96
9-12	500	50,000	.90
Total	10,500	350,000	

Calculate the value of $GRR-NRR$.

2-20. You are given the following information concerning a population study of Country X in 1980.

Age Group	Male	Female	Both Sexes
0-5	4.3	4.0	8.3
5-15	8.5	8.2	16.7
15-20	4.7	4.5	9.2
20-25	4.8	4.7	9.5
25-45	14.6	14.8	29.4
45+	13.3	13.6	26.9
All Ages	50.2	49.8	100.0

Percentage Distribution of Population Country X, July 1, 1980

Percentage of Births by Age Group of Mother Country X, 1980	
Under 20	15.0
20-25	35.0
25 and over	50.0
All ages	100.0

You are also given that crude birth rate in 1980 is 20 births per 1000 population. Determine the age-specific fertility rate in 1980 for women aged 20 through 25.

2-21. The following data were collected for a certain animal species.

Age-Specific Fertility Rates (per 1000)								
Tabulated Age	1975	1976	1977	1978	1979	1980	1981	1982
0	0	0	0	0	0	0	0	0
1	70	60	70	60	70	80	60	70
2	450	400	440	380	410	400	450	420
3	810	820	850	820	830	850	870	850
4	300	270	280	300	280	260	270	240
5	110	120	100	80	100	120	100	80
6	20	30	10	30	20	10	20	20
7+	0	0	0	0	0	0	0	0

For all ages and all years, the sex ratio at birth is 145 males per 100 females. Determine $|X-Y|$, where X is the gross reproduction rate per female for 1980 calculated by the calendar year method, and Y is the gross reproduction rate per female, for females with a tabulated age of 0 in 1975, calculated by the generation method.

CHAPTER 3

THE LIFE TABLE

3.1 INTRODUCTION

An important task for demographers is the periodic construction of a *life table*, a snapshot presentation of the mortality profile of a community at a specific time. The construction of life tables varies from country to country and from time to time, but it is possible to describe, in general terms, a generic method for constructing a life table. This important work will be described in general in Chapter 4, and illustrated with detailed accounts of the construction of the most recent Canadian and U.S. national life tables. Before exploring the topic of constructing life tables from census data, however, we will first give a description of the life table itself as a mathematical model.

The life table model has been in existence for many years, as pointed out in Chapter 1 where we made reference to the early work of Graunt and Halley. It has been described in many textbooks by actuaries, demographers, and other statisticians.

The life table model can be interpreted in either a *deterministic* or a *stochastic framework*. The former has been the traditional framework, as illustrated by Jordan [12]; the latter is a more modern framework, and is given a thorough presentation by Bowers, et al. [4] and London [20]. Although the stochastic approach permits a deeper analysis of the model, an understanding of it requires a familiarity with probability theory which we do not wish to presume here. Therefore this text will present a largely deterministic view of the model.

3.2 LIFE TABLE VALUES

The life table model shows the survival pattern of a hypothetical group of newborn lives. The size of this birth cohort is denoted by ℓ_0, and is called the *radix* of the table. In the abbreviated life table shown in Table 3.1 below, the radix is $\ell_0 = 100,000$.[1]

TABLE 3.1

1985-87 CANADIAN LIFE TABLE FEMALE						
Age x	ℓ_x	d_x	p_x	q_x	L_x	T_x	$\overset{o}{e}_x$
(1)	(2)	(3)	(4)	(5)	(6)	(7)	(8)
0	100,000	678	.99322	.00678	99,415	7,972,923	79.73
1	99,322	62	.99938	.00062	99,286	7,873,508	79.27
2	99,260	41	.99959	.00041	99,235	7,774,222	78.32
3	99,219	30	.99970	.00030	99,204	7,674,987	77.35
4	99,189	25	.99974	.00026	99,175	7,575,783	76.38
5	99,164	22	.99978	.00022	99,153	7,476,608	75.40
6	99,142	18	.99982	.00018	99,133	7,377,455	74.41
7	99,124	16	.99984	.00016	99,116	7,278,323	73.43
8	99,108	14	.99986	.00014	99,101	7,179,207	72.44
9	99,094	13	.99986	.00014	99,087	7,080,106	71.45
10	99,081	15	.99986	.00014	99,073	6,981,018	70.46
11	99,066	15	.99985	.00015	99,059	6,881,945	69.47
12	99,051	17	.99982	.00018	99,043	6,782,886	68.48
13	99,034	21	.99979	.00021	99,023	6,683,844	67.49
14	99,013	27	.99973	.00027	98,999	6,584,820	66.50

Column (2) of Table 3.1 shows the number surviving to each successive age, out of the original hypothetical birth cohort. Thus the ℓ_x function gives the number of persons alive at exact age x, according to the model, so we can say that the sequence of ℓ_x values shows the survival pattern of this hypothetical group.

Column (3) shows the number dying at each age last birthday, which is the difference between adjacent values of ℓ_x. Then

---

[1]The complete life table from which Table 3.1 is excerpted is given in Appendix C.

$$d_0 = \ell_0 - \ell_1 \tag{3.1a}$$

or, in general,

$$d_x = \ell_x - \ell_{x+1}. \tag{3.1b}$$

Example 3.1

Prove that in a life table $\ell_0 = \sum_{y=0}^{\infty} d_y$.

Solution

From Equation (3.1) we know that $d_x = \ell_x - \ell_{x+1}$. In particular, $d_0 = \ell_0 - \ell_1$, $d_1 = \ell_1 - \ell_2$, $d_2 = \ell_2 - \ell_3$, and so on. This continues until we reach some age, usually denoted by ω, where $\ell_\omega = 0$. Summing these equations we find $\sum_{y=0}^{\infty} d_y = \ell_0$. Similarly, for any other value of x, $\ell_x = \sum_{t=0}^{\infty} d_{x+t}$. $\qquad\square$

The *probability of survival* from age x to age $x+1$ is denoted by p_x, and is given by

$$p_x = \frac{\ell_{x+1}}{\ell_x}. \tag{3.2}$$

Values of p_x are shown in Column (4).

Similarly, the *probability of death* prior to age $x+1$, for a person alive at age x, is denoted by q_x and given by

$$q_x = \frac{d_x}{\ell_x}. \tag{3.3}$$

Since $d_x = \ell_x - \ell_{x+1}$ from Equation (3.1b), it follows that

$$q_x = \frac{\ell_x - \ell_{x+1}}{\ell_x} = 1 - p_x, \tag{3.4}$$

making use of the definition of p_x from Equation (3.2). Values of q_x are shown in Column (5) of Table 3.1.

Example 3.2

Use Table 3.1 to find each of the following probabilities.
(a)   The probability a newborn survives to age 7
(b)   The probability a newborn dies between ages 7 and 8
(c)   The probability a life aged 7 survives to age 12
(d)   The probability a life aged 7 dies between ages 12 and 14

(a) Survival from birth to age 7 requires survival through all years prior to age 7, so the probability is given by

$$p_0 \cdot p_1 \cdot p_2 \cdot p_3 \cdot p_4 \cdot p_5 \cdot p_6 \; = \; .991245.$$

It is easier to calculate the probability by seeing that it is given by the ratio of the number of survivors at age 7, ℓ_7, to the number of births, ℓ_0. Then the probability is given by

$$_7p_0 \; = \; \frac{\ell_7}{\ell_0} \; = \; .99124. \; [2]$$

(b) This is the product of the probability $_7p_0$, developed in part (a), and q_7. Thus we have $(.99124)(.00016) = .000158598$, or .00016 to 5 decimals. Since $_7p_0 = \dfrac{\ell_7}{\ell_0}$ and $q_7 = \dfrac{d_7}{\ell_7}$, the probability is also given by

$$\frac{\ell_7}{\ell_0} \cdot \frac{d_7}{\ell_7} \; = \; \frac{d_7}{\ell_0} \; = \; .00016.$$

(c) As in part (a), $_5p_7 \; = \; \displaystyle\prod_{x=7}^{11} p_x \; = \; \frac{\ell_{12}}{\ell_7} \; = \; \frac{99051}{99124} \; = \; .99926.$

(d) This is given by $_5p_7(1 - {_2p_{12}})$

$$= \frac{\ell_{12}}{\ell_7}\Big(1 - \frac{\ell_{14}}{\ell_{12}}\Big) = \frac{\ell_{12} - \ell_{14}}{\ell_7} = \frac{99051 - 99013}{99124} = .00038. \qquad \square$$

The life table function in Column (6), denoted by L_x, represents a new concept. It gives the **number of life-years lived**, by the ℓ_x people who attain age x, over the year of age from x to $x+1$. It is a measure of the extent to which the ℓ_x group is exposed to the risk of death over that year, and is called a measure of *exposure*. L_x has a theoretical relationship with the function ℓ_x that can be clearly seen only when ℓ_x is assumed to be continuous, and this will be explored in the next section. For now, however, we can clarify the meaning of L_x by finding an approximate relationship with ℓ_x. This is shown in the following example.

---

[2]The general notation for the probability is $_tp_x = \dfrac{\ell_{x+t}}{\ell_x}$, or $_xp_0 = \dfrac{\ell_x}{\ell_0}$ when measured from birth. An alternative symbol for $_xp_0$ is $S(x)$, which is used extensively in later chapters.

| Example 3.3 |

For the ℓ_x individuals who survive to age x, determine the approximate number of life-years that will be lived before age $x+1$.

[Solution]

Clearly all the ℓ_{x+1} individuals who survive to age $x+1$ will contribute one full year to the total. For the d_x people who die between ages x and $x+1$, the individual contributions will be various fractions of a year, with an average value denoted by f_x, $0 < f_x < 1$. (Readers should be careful to distinguish this meaning of f_x from that established in Chapter 2 for the fertility rate.) Let us assume that the d_x deaths are uniformly distributed between ages x and $x+1$, so that $f_x = \frac{1}{2}$. Then the total number of life-years lived between ages x and $x+1$ by the ℓ_x people who survive to age x is approximately

$$1 \cdot \ell_{x+1} + \tfrac{1}{2} \cdot d_x = \ell_{x+1} + \tfrac{1}{2}(\ell_x - \ell_{x+1}) = \tfrac{1}{2}(\ell_x + \ell_{x+1}). \qquad \square$$

From Example 3.3 we have the approximate relationships

$$L_x \approx \tfrac{1}{2}(\ell_x + \ell_{x+1}) = \tfrac{1}{2}(\ell_x + \ell_x - d_x)$$
$$= \ell_x - \tfrac{1}{2} \cdot d_x, \qquad (3.5)$$

by assuming the d_x deaths to be distributed uniformly over the age interval x to $x+1$. This concept of **uniform distribution of deaths** is more fully developed in Section 3.4.1.

It is a small step from here to see that *all* future life-years lived by the ℓ_x individuals who survive to age x is given by $L_x + L_{x+1} + L_{x+2} + \cdots$.

We define

$$T_x = L_x + L_{x+1} + L_{x+2} \cdots, \qquad (3.6a)$$

and note that T_x represents the **total future lifetime** of the ℓ_x persons who attain age x. Values of T_x are given in Column (7) of Table 3.1. They can be calculated from

$$T_x = T_{x+1} + L_x, \qquad (3.6b)$$

whereby we start at the ω end of the table and work recursively back to age x.

It then follows that the *average future lifetime* of those individuals who attain age x is

$$\overset{\circ}{e}_x = \frac{T_x}{\ell_x}, \tag{3.7}$$

which is called the *complete expectation of life*. Values of $\overset{\circ}{e}_x$ are given in Column (8) of Table 3.1.

Finally, although it is not displayed in Table 3.1, an important additional life table function is the *central rate of mortality*, denoted by m_x and defined as

$$m_x = \frac{d_x}{L_x}. \tag{3.8}$$

There is a close connection between the central rate in a life table model and the age-specific mortality rate defined in Section 2.3. This connection plays a vital role in the construction of life tables from census data, as we will see in Chapter 4.

3.3 THE CONTINUOUS CASE

As described thus far, the life table functions ℓ_x, d_x, p_x, and q_x are discrete functions, defined only for integral values of x. If we now assume that ℓ_x is a continuous function, a number of additional valuable relationships can be derived. This section will pursue that goal.

In the last section we defined L_x to be the number of life-years lived between ages x and $x+1$ by the ℓ_x individuals who attain age x. Alternatively L_x can be defined as the average number of people alive between ages x and $x+1$, which is given by the average value of ℓ_{x+t} from $t=0$ to $t=1$. Both definitions lead to

$$L_x = \int_0^1 \ell_{x+t}\, dt \tag{3.9}$$

as the exact relationship between L_x and ℓ_x, where ℓ_x is assumed to be continuous and the integral value is assumed to exist.

Given that

$$T_x = \sum_{y=x}^{\infty} L_y \tag{3.6a}$$

and

$$L_x = \int_0^1 \ell_{x+t}\, dt, \tag{3.9}$$

it then follows that

$$T_x = \int_0^\infty \ell_{x+t} \, dt. \tag{3.10}$$

Furthermore, since we have defined

$$\overset{o}{e}_x = \frac{T_x}{\ell_x}, \tag{3.7}$$

we can write

$$\overset{o}{e}_x = \frac{\int_0^\infty \ell_{x+t} \, dt}{\ell_x}. \tag{3.11}$$

The function q_x has been defined as

$$q_x = \frac{d_x}{\ell_x}, \tag{3.3}$$

the **probability** that a life aged x will die within one year. q_x could also be described as the *effective rate* of death over a one-year period for the ℓ_x individuals in a life table who survive to age x. This definition of q_x as a rate is reinforced by the equivalent formula

$$q_x = \frac{\ell_x - \ell_{x+1}}{\ell_x}, \tag{3.4b}$$

which shows that q_x measures the rate of change of the ℓ_x curve over the one-year period from age x to age $x+1$, as illustrated in the following figure.

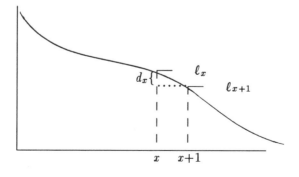

FIGURE 3.1

Figure 3.1 shows that the ℓ_x curve changes (drops) by d_x between x and $x+1$. When this change is divided by the value at the start of the interval, which is ℓ_x, the effective rate of change is produced. Said the other way around, if ℓ_x individuals are exposed to the risk of death for one year, at an effective annual rate of q_x, then d_x individuals will die. Thus we have

$$q_x \cdot \ell_x \cdot 1 \;=\; d_x \;=\; \ell_x - \ell_{x+1}. \tag{3.12}$$

If we measure this effect over a shorter period of time, of length Δt, the resulting formula would be

$$q_x^* \cdot \ell_x \cdot \Delta t \;=\; \ell_x - \ell_{x+\Delta t}, \tag{3.13}$$

leading to

$$q_x^* \;=\; \frac{\ell_x - \ell_{x+\Delta t}}{\ell_x \cdot \Delta t}, \tag{3.14}$$

where q_x^* denotes the effective (annualized) rate of mortality based on the mortality activity in the small interval from x to $x + \Delta t$.

If we then take the limit of Equation (3.14) as $\Delta t \to 0$, we have a measure of the *instantaneous rate of change* at exact age x, which is called the *force of mortality* and is denoted by μ_x. That is

$$\mu_x \;=\; \lim_{\Delta t \to 0} \frac{\ell_x - \ell_{x+\Delta t}}{\ell_x \cdot \Delta t}. \tag{3.15}$$

But $\displaystyle \lim_{\Delta t \to 0} \frac{\ell_{x+\Delta t} - \ell_x}{\Delta t} \;=\; D\ell_x$, the derivative of ℓ_x, so we find that

$$\mu_x \;=\; \frac{-D\ell_x}{\ell_x} \tag{3.16a}$$

$$\;=\; -D \log_e \ell_x. \tag{3.16b}$$

Example 3.4

Given $\mu_x = -D \log_e \ell_x$, show that

$$\ell_x = \ell_0 \cdot exp\left[-\int_0^x \mu_y \, dy \right]. \tag{3.17}$$

Solution

If $\mu_y = -D\log_e \ell_y$, then

$$-\int_0^x \mu_y \, dy = -\int_0^x -D\log_e \ell_y \, dy$$

$$= \log_e \ell_x - \log_e \ell_0 = \log_e \frac{\ell_x}{\ell_0},$$

which leads to

$$\ell_0 \cdot exp\left[-\int_0^x \mu_y \, dy\right] = \ell_0 \cdot exp\left[\log_e \ell_x/\ell_0\right] = \ell_x,$$

which is Equation (3.17). □

From Equation (3.2), $p_x = \frac{\ell_{x+1}}{\ell_x}$. Using Equation (3.17) we have $\ell_x = \ell_0 \cdot exp\left[-\int_0^x \mu_y \, dy\right]$ and $\ell_{x+1} = \ell_0 \cdot exp\left[-\int_0^{x+1} \mu_y \, dy\right]$, so it can be seen that

$$p_x = \frac{\ell_{x+1}}{\ell_x} = exp\left[-\int_x^{x+1} \mu_y \, dy\right] \tag{3.18a}$$

or

$$p_x = exp\left[-\int_0^1 \mu_{x+s} \, ds\right], \tag{3.18b}$$

using the simple variable change $y = x+s$. A generalized version of Equation (3.18b) is

$$_tp_x = exp\left[-\int_0^t \mu_{x+s} \, ds\right]. \tag{3.18c}$$

Example 3.5

Show that $\frac{\partial}{\partial t} \,_tp_x = -\,_tp_x \mu_{x+t}$.

Solution

$\frac{\partial}{\partial t} \,_tp_x = \frac{\partial}{\partial t} \frac{\ell_{x+t}}{\ell_x}$. Since $\mu_x = \frac{-D\ell_x}{\ell_x}$, we see that $D\ell_x = -\ell_x \mu_x$, and, similarly, $\frac{\partial}{\partial t} \ell_{x+t} = -\ell_{x+t} \mu_{x+t}$. Thus we find

$$\frac{\partial}{\partial t} \,_tp_x = \frac{-\ell_{x+t} \mu_{x+t}}{\ell_x} = -\,_tp_x \mu_{x+t}.$$

(An alternative approach is to differentiate Equation (3.18c).) □

| Example 3.6 |

A life aged 30 is subject to an extra hazard during the next year. The normal probability of survival, p_{30}, is .993 and the extra risk may be expressed as an addition of .06 to the normal force of mortality over that interval. Find q'_{30}, the probability of dying between age 30 and age 31 for this particular life.

| Solution |

From Equation (3.18b) we have $p_{30} = exp\left[-\int_0^1 \mu_{30+s} \, ds\right]$, so it follows that

$$p'_{30} = exp\left[-\int_0^1 \mu'_{30+s} \, ds\right]$$

$$= exp\left[-\int_0^1 (\mu_{30+s} + .06) \, ds\right]$$

$$= p_{30} \cdot e^{-.06}$$

$$= .9351722.$$

Then we find $q'_{30} = 1 - p'_{30} = .0648278.$ □

| Example 3.7 |

Show that

$$\int_x^{x+n} \ell_y \mu_y \, dy = \ell_x - \ell_{x+n}. \qquad (3.19)$$

| Solution |

From Equation (3.16a) we have $\mu_x = \dfrac{-D\ell_x}{\ell_x}$, so that $\ell_x \mu_x = -D\ell_x$. Then

$$\int_x^{x+n} \ell_y \mu_y \, dy = -\int_x^{x+n} D\ell_y \, dy$$

$$= -\ell_y\Big|_x^{x+n}$$

$$= \ell_x - \ell_{x+n}. \qquad □$$

Several important formulas follow from Example 3.7. Since $d_x = \ell_x - \ell_{x+1}$, we see that

$$d_x = \int_x^{x+1} \ell_y \mu_y \, dy = \int_0^1 \ell_{x+t} \mu_{x+t} \, dt. \tag{3.20}$$

Consistent with previous notation, we now define

$$_n q_x = \frac{n d_x}{\ell_x} = \frac{\ell_x - \ell_{x+n}}{\ell_x}. \tag{3.21}$$

Using Equation (3.19), with the change of variable $y = x+t$, we have

$$_n q_x = \frac{\int_0^n \ell_{x+t} \mu_{x+t} \, dt}{\ell_x}$$

$$= \int_0^n {}_t p_x \mu_{x+t} \, dt, \tag{3.22}$$

which has an important statistical interpretation.

In stochastic contingency theory, the random variable T denotes the (random) future time of death for a person age x, and the function $_t p_x \mu_{x+t}$ is the **probability density function**, usually denoted $f(t)$, of the random variable T. It then follows that $_n q_x = \int_0^n {}_t p_x \mu_{x+t} \, dt = \int_0^n f(t) \, dt$ is the **cumulative distribution function**, usually denoted $F(n)$, which gives the probability that the time of death for a life aged x will be prior to time n.

In earlier discussions the complete expectation of life, $\overset{o}{e}_x$, was defined as

$$\overset{o}{e}_x = \frac{T_x}{\ell_x} \tag{3.7}$$

$$= \frac{\int_0^\infty \ell_{x+t} \, dt}{\ell_x} \tag{3.11}$$

$$= \int_0^\infty {}_t p_x \, dt. \tag{3.23}$$

We can now derive an expression for $\overset{o}{e}_x$ using a more statistical approach. Since $\overset{o}{e}_x$ is the expected future lifetime of a person aged x, and since T is the random variable for that future lifetime, it follows that $\overset{o}{e}_x$ is the *expected value* of T, denoted by $E[T]$. But we know that $f(t) = {}_tp_x\mu_{x+t}$ is the probability density function of T, so the expected value of T is therefore given by

$$\overset{o}{e}_x = E[T] = \int_0^\infty t \cdot f(t) \; dt = \int_0^\infty t \cdot {}_tp_x\mu_{x+t} \; dt. \qquad (3.24)$$

Example 3.8

Show that $\int_0^\infty t \cdot {}_tp_x\mu_{x+t} \; dt = \int_0^\infty {}_tp_x \; dt$, which shows that Equations (3.24) and (3.23) are consistent definitions for $\overset{o}{e}_x$.

Solution

For $\int_0^\infty t \cdot {}_tp_x\mu_{x+t} \; dt$ we use integration by parts, recalling from Example 3.5 that $\frac{\partial}{\partial t}{}_tp_x = -{}_tp_x\mu_{x+t}$. Then we have

$$\int_0^\infty \underbrace{t}_{\frac{d}{dt}} \; \underbrace{\left| \begin{array}{c} {}_tp_x\mu_{x+t} \; dt \\ -{}_tp_x \end{array} \right.} = \left. -t \cdot {}_tp_x \right|_0^\infty + \int_0^\infty {}_tp_x \; dt = \int_0^\infty {}_tp_x \; dt,$$

since $-t \cdot {}_tp_x$ evaluates to zero at both limits.   □

Given this statistical framework, we could also formulate the *variance* of T, the random future lifetime, as

$$Var(T) = \int_0^\infty t^2 \cdot {}_tp_x\mu_{x+t} \; dt - \left(\overset{o}{e}_x\right)^2, \qquad (3.25)$$

since we know that $Var(T) = E[T^2] - (E[T])^2$.

3.4   METHODS FOR FRACTIONAL AGES

On occasion we require the value, at a fractional age, of a life table function that is given at integral ages only. For example, the table gives values of ℓ_x only for integral x, and values of ${}_np_x$ only for integral x and n. Suppose we seek the value of ${}_tp_x$ for a fractional value of t. How might we proceed?

Two methods are widely used to estimate life table values at fractional ages.

3.4.1 Uniform Distribution of Deaths

If there are d_x deaths between ages x and $x+1$ then, under the assumption of a **uniform distribution of deaths** (UDD), there will be $t \cdot d_x$ deaths prior to time t in that age interval, where $0 < t < 1$. Then the number alive at age $x+t$ is given by

$$\ell_{x+t} = \ell_x - t \cdot d_x, \tag{3.26}$$

which can be rewritten as

$$\ell_{x+t} = \ell_x - t(\ell_x - \ell_{x+1}) \tag{3.27a}$$

$$= (1-t)\,\ell_x + t \cdot \ell_{x+1}. \tag{3.27b}$$

The reader should recognize this as a linear interpolation formula, showing that the assumption of a uniform distribution of deaths is equivalent to a linear interpolation between ℓ_x and ℓ_{x+1}. This implies that we are assuming the ℓ_x curve to be a straight line from x to $x+1$.

Note that this is not the same as an assumption that ℓ_x is linear from 0 to ω. The assumption of uniform distribution of deaths assumes linearity only over each year of age, and is therefore a much more accurate representation of ℓ_x.

| Example 3.9 |

Confirm that the approximate relationship $L_x \approx \ell_x - \frac{1}{2} \cdot d_x$, given by Equation (3.5), is exact under the uniform distribution of deaths assumption.

| Solution |

From Equation (3.9) we have $L_x = \int_0^1 \ell_{x+t}\ dt$. But under UDD we have $\ell_{x+t} = \ell_x - t \cdot d_x$, for $0 < t < 1$. Thus we find

$$L_x = \int_0^1 \ell_x - t \cdot d_x\ dt$$

$$= t \cdot \ell_x - \frac{1}{2} t^2 \cdot d_x \Big|_0^1$$

$$= \ell_x - \frac{1}{2} \cdot d_x. \qquad \square$$

Example 3.10

Show that $_tq_x = t \cdot q_x$, $0 < t < 1$, under the UDD assumption.

Solution

Generalizing Equation (3.4a) we have $_tq_x = 1 - \dfrac{\ell_{x+t}}{\ell_x} = \dfrac{\ell_x - \ell_{x+t}}{\ell_x}$,

and from Equation (3.26) we have $\ell_{x+t} = \ell_x - t \cdot d_x$, $0 < t < 1$. Thus we find

$$_tq_x = \frac{\ell_x - (\ell_x - t \cdot d_x)}{\ell_x}$$

$$= \frac{t \cdot d_x}{\ell_x}$$

$$= t \cdot q_x. \qquad \qquad \Box$$

Example 3.11

Show that $_tp_x \mu_{x+t} = q_x$ under the UDD assumption.

Solution

From Example 3.5 we know that

$$_tp_x \mu_{x+t} = -\frac{\partial}{\partial t} \,_tp_x,$$

and from Example 3.10 we have $_tp_x = 1 - t \cdot q_x$. Substituting we find

$$_tp_x \mu_{x+t} = -\frac{\partial}{\partial t}(1 - t \cdot q_x) = q_x. \qquad \qquad \Box$$

3.4.2 Constant Force of Mortality

Another popular method for deriving life table values at fractional durations is to assume that the force of mortality, μ_{x+t}, is constant for $0 < t < 1$.

Example 3.12

Assume that μ_{x+t} is constant and equal to μ from age x to age $x+1$. Show that $q_x = 1 - e^{-\mu}$.

Solution

We know that $q_x = 1 - exp\left[-\int_0^1 \mu_{x+t}\, dt\right]$ from Equations (3.4b) and (3.18b). But if $\mu_{x+t} = \mu$ from age x to age $x+1$, then we have

$$q_x = 1 - exp\left[-\int_0^1 \mu\, dt\right]$$

$$= 1 - exp\left[-\mu t\, \Big|_0^1\right]$$

$$= 1 - e^{-\mu}. \qquad \square$$

Example 3.13

Assuming a constant force of mortality from age x to age $x+1$, show that $m_x = \mu$.

Solution

From Equation (3.8) we have $m_x = \dfrac{d_x}{L_x}$, where $d_x = \int_0^1 \ell_{x+t}\, \mu_{x+t}\, dt$ from Equation (3.20), and $L_x = \int_0^1 \ell_{x+t}\, dt$ from Equation (3.9). But if $\mu_{x+t} = \mu$ for $0 < t < 1$, then we have

$$m_x = \frac{\int_0^1 \ell_{x+t} \cdot \mu\, dt}{\int_0^1 \ell_{x+t}\, dt}$$

$$= \mu\, \frac{\int_0^1 \ell_{x+t}\, dt}{\int_0^1 \ell_{x+t}\, dt}$$

$$= \mu. \qquad \square$$

Combining the results of Examples 3.12 and 3.13 we find an interesting transition equation to go from m_x to q_x, which we will find useful in constructing a life table. Since $q_x = 1 - e^{-\mu}$ and $m_x = \mu$, then it follows that

$$q_x = 1 - e^{-m_x}, \qquad (3.28)$$

under the assumption of a constant force of mortality.

Example 3.14

Show that $p_x = (_tp_x)^{1/t}$ under the constant force of mortality assumption.

Solution

From Equation (3.18b) we have $p_x = exp\left[-\int_0^1 \mu_{x+s}\, ds\right] = e^{-\mu}$, under the constant force assumption. Similarly,

$$_tp_x = exp\left[-\int_0^t \mu_{x+s}\, ds\right] = e^{-t \cdot \mu} = (e^{-\mu})^t,$$

under the constant force assumption, so we have $p_x = (_tp_x)^{1/t}$, as required. $\square$

Example 3.15

Find an expression for f_x, as defined in Example 3.3, assuming a constant force of mortality.

Solution

f_x was defined in Example 3.3 as the average fraction of the year lived by the d_x people who die between ages x and $x+1$. (It should be intuitive that $f_x = \frac{1}{2}$ under the UDD assumption.)

In general,

$$f_x = \frac{\int_0^1 t \cdot \ell_{x+t}\, \mu_{x+t}\, dt}{d_x}$$

$$= \frac{\ell_x}{d_x}\int_0^1 t \cdot {}_tp_x\, \mu_{x+t}\, dt. \qquad (3.29)$$

Under the constant force assumption,

$$f_x = \frac{\ell_x}{d_x}\int_0^1 t \cdot e^{-\mu t} \cdot \mu\, dt$$

$$= \frac{\mu}{1-e^{-\mu}}\int_0^1 t \cdot e^{-\mu t}\, dt,$$

since $\frac{\ell_x}{d_x} = \frac{1}{q_x} = \frac{1}{1-e^{-\mu}}$. Using integration by parts we have

$$f_x = \frac{\mu}{1-e^{-\mu}} \int_0^1 t \left| \frac{e^{-\mu t}}{dt} \right| \frac{dt}{-\frac{1}{\mu} e^{-\mu t}}$$

$$= \frac{\mu}{1-e^{-\mu}} \left[-\frac{t}{\mu} \cdot e^{-\mu t} \Big|_0^1 + \frac{1}{\mu} \int_0^1 e^{-\mu t} \, dt \right]$$

$$= \frac{1}{1-e^{-\mu}} \left[-t \cdot e^{-\mu t} \Big|_0^1 - \frac{1}{\mu} \cdot e^{-\mu t} \Big|_0^1 \right]$$

$$= \frac{1}{1-e^{-\mu}} \left[-e^{-\mu} - \frac{1}{\mu} \cdot e^{-\mu} + \frac{1}{\mu} \right]$$

$$= \frac{1}{1-e^{-\mu}} \left[-e^{-\mu} + \frac{1}{\mu}(1-e^{-\mu}) \right]$$

$$= \frac{1}{\mu} - \frac{e^{-\mu}}{1-e^{-\mu}}. \qquad (3.30)$$

□

Example 3.16

Show that Equation (3.30) can also be written as

$$f_x = -\frac{1}{\ln p_x} - \frac{p_x}{1-p_x}. \qquad (3.31)$$

Solution

From Example 3.12 we have $p_x = e^{-\mu}$, so that $\mu = -\ln p_x$, under the constant force assumption. Then Equation (3.30) directly becomes

$$f_x = -\frac{1}{\ln p_x} - \frac{p_x}{1-p_x}. \qquad □$$

3.6 EXERCISES

3.1 Introduction;   3.2 Life Table Values

3-1. A life table is defined by the following values of m_x.

x	m_x
0	.05
1	.10
2	.30
3	.50
4	2.00

(a) Find corresponding values of q_x assuming a uniform distribution of deaths.

(b) Do a complete life table, including the seven functions shown in Table 3.1, using a radix of $\ell_0 = 1000$.

(c) What is the value of ω in this table?

(d) Verify that $\sum_{y=0}^{\infty} d_y = \ell_0$.

3-2. From the life table developed in Exercise 3-1, calculate each of the following.

(a) $_3d_0$ (b) $_2q_1$ (c) $_3p_1$

3-3. Use Table 3.1 to calculate each of the following.

(a) $_2q_1$

(b) $_3p_1$

(c) The probability a life aged 4 dies between ages 9 and 12

(d) The probability a newborn dies between ages 10 and 14

(e) The expected number of survivors at age 12 out of 500 females alive at age 3

3.3 The Continuous Case

3-4. Find $\dfrac{\partial}{\partial x}\ _tp_x$.

3-5. Show that (a) $\frac{d}{dx}\overset{\circ}{e}_x = \mu_x\overset{\circ}{e}_x - 1$. Use this result to show that

(b) $\mu_x = \frac{1}{\overset{\circ}{e}_x} + \frac{1}{\overset{\circ}{e}_x}\cdot\frac{d}{dx}\overset{\circ}{e}_x \approx \frac{1}{\overset{\circ}{e}_x}\left[1 + \frac{1}{2}(\overset{\circ}{e}_{x+1} - \overset{\circ}{e}_{x-1})\right]$.

3-6. Suppose $\mu'_{40} = \mu_{40} - k$ for year of age 40 to 41 only. Given $_{30}P_{40} = .675$ and $_{30}P'_{40} = .725$, find k.

3-7. Obtain an expression for ℓ_x if $\mu_x = \frac{1}{100-x}$, for $x < 100$.

3-8. Show that $\frac{d}{dt}\,_tp_x\overset{\circ}{e}_{x+t} = -\,_tp_x$.

3-9. Find $\frac{d}{dx}\log_e T_x$.

3-10. Given that $\mu'_x = \mu_x + \frac{.08}{\overset{\circ}{e}_x}$ for all x, find ℓ'_x.

3-11. Show that $L_{x+1} = L_x \cdot exp\left[-\int_x^{x+1} m_y \; dy\right]$.

3.4 Methods for Fractional Ages

3-12. A group of 1000 light bulbs is subject to discrete probabilities of failure given by $q_x = .2(1+x)$, for $x = 0, 1, \ldots, 4$. Assuming a uniform distribution of failures within any year, calculate a complete life table for these light bulbs.

3-13. Assume the force of mortality μ_x is constant and equal to μ for $x \geq 65$, and that $\overset{\circ}{e}_{65} = 20$. Find q_{65}.

3-14. Given that $m_x = .7$, calculate q_x under each of the following assumptions.

(a) Uniform distribution of deaths
(b) Constant force of mortality

3-15. Define $\overset{\circ}{e}_{x:\overline{n}|}$ as the expected future lifetime, for a person age x, between ages x and $x+n$. Explain the formula

$$\overset{\circ}{e}_{x:\overline{n}|} = \int_0^n t \cdot {}_tp_x\mu_{x+t}\; dt + n \cdot {}_np_x,$$

and show that $\overset{\circ}{e}_{x:\overline{n}|} = \int_0^n {}_tp_x\; dt.$

3-16. Given the values $\ell_{65} = 6000$ and $\ell_{66} = 5916$, find $\mu_{65.25}$ under each of the following assumptions.

(a) Uniform distribution of deaths
(b) Constant force of mortality

3-17. Given the life table values $\ell_{65} = 86{,}109$, $\ell_{84} = 44{,}241$, and $\ell_{85} = 40{,}633$, find the median future lifetime for a person aged 65 under each of the following assumptions.

(a) Uniform distribution of deaths
(b) Constant force of mortality

CHAPTER 4

CONSTRUCTION OF LIFE TABLES FROM CENSUS DATA

4.1 INTRODUCTION

In Chapter 3 we introduced the life table, a mathematical model showing the survival pattern of a hypothetical birth cohort. In this chapter we will explore methods by which such models can be constructed from demographic data.

From the discussion of the model itself in Section 3.2 it should be clear that all of the columns, in a typical life table, such as the one illustrated in Table 3.1, can be derived from a set of mortality probabilities q_x, for $x = 0, 1, \ldots$, and an arbitrary table radix ℓ_0. Beginning with ℓ_0 and q_0 we would first find

$$d_0 = \ell_0 \cdot q_0, \qquad (4.1a)$$

followed by

$$\ell_1 = \ell_0 - d_0. \qquad (4.2a)$$

When used recursively we would find

$$d_x = \ell_x \cdot q_x, \qquad (4.1b)$$

and

$$\ell_{x+1} = \ell_x - d_x \qquad (4.2b)$$

for $x = 1, 2, \ldots$. Values of p_x are found directly as

$$p_x \; = \; 1 - q_x, \qquad\qquad (4.3)$$

and values of L_x are usually found from the uniform distribution of deaths relationship

$$L_x \; = \; \ell_x - \tfrac{1}{2} \cdot d_x, \qquad\qquad (4.4)$$

which was derived in Example 3.9. Then values of T_x and $\overset{o}{e}_x$ follow directly from L_x.

This discussion shows that a generic approach to constructing a specific table requires only a table radix and a set of age-specific mortality probabilities. When the table is constructed from census data, however, it is customary to begin with central rates of mortality, rather than mortality probabilities. This requires an additional step in the table construction process, as described below.

Chapter 2 defined the crude death rate as the number of deaths observed in a year divided by the midyear population, and described how this rate could be made age and sex specific. A set of age and sex specific crude death rates is the starting point for constructing a life table from the population data of a particular community.

Let $_nD_x$ denote the deaths in a year in a chosen population, occurring between ages x and $x+n$. (In most applications there would be two separate values of $_nD_x$, say $_nD_x^f$ and $_nD_x^m$, denoting female and male deaths respectively. Here we use simply $_nD_x$ to suggest that the procedure is the same in either case.) Let $_nP_x$ denote the enumerated midyear population aged x to $x+n$. Then

$$_nM_x \; = \; \frac{_nD_x}{_nP_x} \qquad\qquad (4.5a)$$

is the crude (central) death rate for persons in that age range.

Because the number of deaths in one year is fairly small at many ages, demographers generally use the average number of deaths over several years in the numerator of Equation (4.5a). For example, the national life tables of both Canada and the United States are based on observed deaths over a three-year period.

When a three-year period is used for the deaths in the numerator, the population count used in the denominator should be taken on July 1 of the middle year. For reasons explained in Chapter 1, the Canadian census count is taken on June 1 and the U.S. count is taken on April 1. However, no adjustments are made to this population count, even though it is not at the exact mid-point of the three-year study period.

In constructing a life table from the crude central death rates of a population, it is common to use rates applicable to the one-year age interval x to $x+1$, rather than the n-year interval x to $x+n$. It is possible to derive such one-year rates directly from population data as

$$M_x = \frac{D_x}{P_x}, \tag{4.5b}$$

where D_x denotes the observed deaths between ages x and $x+1$, and P_x is the midperiod population in that same age range. Normally, however, the one-year rates are obtained from a sequence of n-year rates by interpolation, or some other approximation method.

By whichever method obtained, a sequence of one-year crude central death rates would be further modified to adjust for errors, anomalies, and lack of smooth and logical progression from one age to the next. (This modification is known in actuarial work as *graduation* and is not discussed further in this text. The interested reader is referred to London [19].)

The graduated one-year central death rates will be denoted by m_x, to distinguish them from the sequence of population crude death rates M_x (or $_nM_x$) from which they were derived. This sequence of m_x values, for $x = 0, 1, \cdots$, is then used to construct a life table which summarizes the mortality characteristics of the population from which the original M_x were obtained.

From the sequence of m_x values we could obtain the corresponding sequence of q_x values by the relationship

$$q_x = 1 - e^{-m_x}, \tag{4.6}$$

developed in Section 3.4.2 under the constant force of mortality assumption. Alternatively, using the uniform distribution of deaths assumption, we have

$$m_x = \frac{d_x}{L_x} = \frac{d_x}{\ell_x - \frac{1}{2} \cdot d_x} = \frac{q_x}{1 - \frac{1}{2} \cdot q_x}, \tag{4.7}$$

making use of Equation (4.4). Solving Equation (4.7) for q_x we obtain

$$q_x = \frac{m_x}{1 + \frac{1}{2} \cdot m_x}. \tag{4.8}$$

From this sequence of q_x values, along with an arbitrary radix, the entire life table can now be derived, as described above.

The generic construction method described in this section will usually be modified in any specific case. This is illustrated in the following two sections where we present the detailed construction of the most recent national life tables in the United States and Canada.

4.2 THE 1979-81 U.S. LIFE TABLES

National and State Life Tables are produced decennially in the United States, based on census data and reported births and deaths. The committee responsible for their construction must deal with a variety of issues beyond the mere calculation of the table entries. For example, how are errors in the census data and in the vital statistics on death to be handled? Of the 5.9 million deaths reported, 1834 were reported without an age. These deaths were distributed among the various ages in proportion to the deaths properly reported.

No specific adjustments were made for possible incompleteness in the enumeration of the population, the registration of births and deaths, or the possible misreporting of age.

The data used were the reported deaths for 1979-1981, census data adjusted by the Census Bureau for April 1, 1980, and births for 1977-81.

The data are given by single ages up to and including age 5, in quinquennial age groupings from age 5 to 99 (so that age 5 is in twice), and a final grouping for those age 100 and over, where "age" means age last birthday. Data for ages under 1 year were further divided into groupings of under 1 day, 1-7 days, 7-28 days, and 28-365 days.

April 1 populations were used as if they were July 1 populations, which was the midpoint of the exposure period. The radix was chosen as $\ell_0 = 100,000$.

4.2.1 Ages Under 2 Years

At ages under 2 years, values of $_t d_x$ were calculated as

$$_t d_x = \ell_0 \cdot \frac{_t D_x}{_t E_x}, \tag{4.9}$$

where $_tD_x$ is the number of reported deaths between exact ages x and $x+t$, and $_tE_x$ represents the lives exposed to the risk of death in that age interval. The values of $_tE_x$ were determined from birth records, as shown in the following table. (The reasons for using births as the measure of exposure were described in Chapter 2.)

TABLE 4.1

Age at Death	$_tE_x$
Under 1 day [0,1)	$\frac{1}{730}(B^{78}+730B^{79}+730B^{80}+729B^{81})$
1-7 days [1,7)	$\frac{1}{730}(8B^{78}+730B^{79}+730B^{80}+722B^{81})$
7-28 days [7,28)	$\frac{1}{730}(35B^{78}+730B^{79}+730B^{80}+695B^{81})$
28-365 days [28,365)	$\frac{1}{730}(393B^{78}+730B^{79}+730B^{80}+337B^{81})$
1-2 years [1,2)	$\frac{1}{2}(B^{77}+2B^{78}+2B^{79}+B^{80})$

The coefficients assigned to the birth data to determine the Table 4.1 exposure values require some explanation.

Consider first the exposure $\frac{1}{730}(B^{78}+730B^{79}+730B^{80}+729B^{81})$, which is associated with the deaths in the first day of life.

The numerator of Equation (4.9) consists of deaths at ages under one day observed in the period 1979 to 1981, so the denominator must represent the births that could potentially give rise to these deaths. It follows that no birth prior to December 31, 1978 is eligible for consideration. Assuming a uniform distribution of events (births and deaths), then, on average, one-half of the births of December 31, 1978 could die in the first day of life during the exposure period 1979 to 1981. Thus "half a day's worth" of births from the 1978 total are included, which is $\frac{1}{730}B^{78}$.

Similarly, one-half of the births of December 31, 1981 dying in the first day of life will die in 1982, which is outside the exposure period, so we exclude "half a day's worth" of births from the 1981 total, which is $\frac{1}{730}B^{81}$, leaving $\frac{729}{730}B^{81}$.

Consider next the exposure associated with deaths in the age interval 7-28 days. Anyone born after December 24, 1978 who dies at age 7-28 days will die in 1979 and should be included in the exposure, so the births of the last seven days of 1978 are *fully* included in the exposure formula. The births of the previous 21 days of 1978 (*i.e.*, December 4 to December 24 inclusive) will have a fifty-fifty chance of dying at age 7-27 days in 1979 versus 1978. Thus there are an additional 21 days (28 minus 7) of 1978 whose births require an exposure of $\frac{1}{2}$ in the formula. Then in total the exposure for 1978 births is $\frac{7}{365} + \frac{1}{2}\left(\frac{21}{365}\right) = \frac{35}{730}$.

Similarly, the exposure from the 1981 births must be decreased by $\frac{35}{730}B^{81}$, leaving $\frac{695}{730}B^{81}$.

Example 4.1

Show that for deaths at ages between exactly a days and b days, in general, the exposure formula is $\frac{a+b}{730}B^{78} + B^{79} + B^{80} + \left(1 - \frac{a+b}{730}\right)B^{81}$.

Solution

As explained above, the births of the last a days of 1978 qualify for full inclusion in the exposure, and the births of the previous $(b-a)$ days receive an exposure of $\frac{1}{2}$ per day. Thus the exposure associated with 1978 births is $a + \frac{1}{2}(b-a) = \frac{1}{2}(a+b)$ days, which is $\left(\frac{a+b}{730}\right)^{th}$ of the year. The exposure for 1981 births is decreased by $a + \frac{1}{2}(b-a)$ days, leaving $\left(1 - \frac{a+b}{730}\right)B^{81}$ as the correct exposure.   □

4.2.2 Ages 2 to 4 and 5 to 94 Years

Mortality rates at ages 2 to 94 were derived using Equation (4.8) and the previously calculated values of m_x to obtain

$$q_x = \frac{m_x}{1 + \frac{1}{2}m_x}. \tag{4.8}$$

At ages 5 to 94, the values of m_x were obtained as

$$m_x = \frac{D_x^{79-81}}{3 \cdot P_x(80)}, \tag{4.10a}$$

where D_x^{79-81} is the reported deaths in the study period at age x last birthday and $P_x(80)$ is the April 1, 1980 census count at age x, used to approximate the midyear population.

At ages 2 to 4, however, it was felt that the accuracy of the m_x values would be improved by using

$$m_x = \frac{D_x^{79-81}}{P_{x-1}(80) + P_x(80) + P_{x+1}(80)}, \qquad (4.10b)$$

to better reflect the three birth cohorts from which the exposed population arose.

| Example 4.2 |

Show that if $q_x = \dfrac{m_x}{1 + \frac{1}{2} \cdot m_x}$ and $m_x = \dfrac{D_x^{79-81}}{P_{x-1}(80) + P_x(80) + P_{x+1}(80)}$,

then $q_x = \dfrac{D_x^{79-81}}{P_{x-1}(80) + P_x(80) + P_{x+1}(80) + \frac{1}{2} \cdot D_x^{79-81}}$.

| Solution |

Substituting the formula for m_x directly into the q_x formula we obtain

$$q_x = \frac{\dfrac{D_x^{79-81}}{P_{x-1}(80) + P_x(80) + P_{x+1}(80)}}{1 + \dfrac{1}{2}\left(\dfrac{D_x^{79-81}}{P_{x-1}(80) + P_x(80) + P_{x+1}(80)}\right)}$$

$$= \frac{D_x^{79-81}}{P_{x-1}(80) + P_x(80) + P_{x+1}(80) + \frac{1}{2} \cdot D_x^{79-81}}. \qquad \square$$

Special modifications were made to the q_x values at ages 85 and over. Although these changes are specific to the 1979-81 U.S. Life Tables, they reflect the general ingenuity of demographers in using all available data to establish best estimates of unknown values.

4.2.3 Ages Over 94 Years

Data on populations at advanced ages are often subject to error. Not only do we find the normal reporting and misstatement of age problems discussed in Chapter 1, but there may also be some motivation to deliberately report incorrect age data. Because many economic advantages accrue to those beyond a defined age, such as Medicare, bus passes, and so on, there may be an upward bias in the reporting of ages near the qualifying criterion. At more advanced ages there may be a certain social status attached to longevity that again leads to an upward bias. For whatever the reason, age statistics at advanced ages are often suspect.

In order to qualify for Medicare in the U.S., age 65 must be proven, a requirement that has existed since 1966. It is therefore believed that Medicare data are more reliable than census or vital statistics data for those at advanced ages. Thus for ages 95 and over, mortality rates in the 1979-81 U.S. Life Table are based on the experience of the Medicare program, as provided by the Office of the Actuary, U.S. Social Security Administration. The Medicare data produced values of q_x directly, without first finding m_x.

Rates from the Medicare data were actually produced for ages 85 and higher, and rates from the census data were produced at ages 94 and lower. To facilitate a smooth transition from census-based rates to Medicare-based rates, the values of q_x for ages 85 to 94 were developed as a blend of the two, using

$$q_x = \frac{1}{11}\left[(95-x)\,q_x^C + (x-84)\,q_x^M\right]. \tag{4.11}$$

Thus the final table rates are based on census data for ages through 84, on Medicare data for ages 95 and higher, and on a blend of the two for ages 85 through 94.

At all ages, the mortality rates actually used were not the crude values calculated directly from the source data, but rather a set of graduated rates, as described in Section 4.1.[1]

It was decided to have the graduated q_x values approach $q_x = 1$, while never actually reaching it. Accordingly, the graduated rates at certain older ages were rejected and replaced by rates obtained by an extrapolation formula.

The q_x curve tends to flatten out at advanced ages so that the ratio $\frac{q_{x+1}}{q_x}$ tends to decline. For the 1979-81 Life Tables, the last actual rate retained was the one at the youngest age y such

---

[1]For a detailed description of the graduation process, refer to "U.S. Decennial Life Tables for 1979-81, Vol. 1, No. 3," U.S. Department of Health and Human Services, May 1987.

that $\dfrac{\frac{q_{y+1}}{q_y} - 1}{\frac{q_y}{q_{y-1}} - 1} < .9$. Thereafter the mortality rates were extrapo-

lated to age 111 by the relationship $\frac{q_{x+1}}{q_x} - 1 = .9\left(\frac{q_x}{q_{x-1}} - 1\right)$, so that

$$q_{x+1} = q_x\left[.9\left(\frac{q_x}{q_{x-1}} - 1\right) + 1\right]. \tag{4.12}$$

This procedure is illustrated in Example 4.3.

Finally, the Medicare-based values, which were on an age-nearest-birthday basis, were adjusted to an age-last-birthday basis, to be consistent with the census-based values. The last value produced was q_{109}.

Example 4.3

Given the following data representing 1988 ungraduated Medicare mortality rates, find the value of q_{98} produced by the methodology of the 1979-81 U.S. Life Tables.

Age	q_x
94	.20463
95	.21801
96	.23211
97	.24310
98	.25264
99	.25879

Solution

First we develop the test values shown in Column (4) of the following table

Age	q_x	$\frac{q_{x+1}}{q_x}$	$\dfrac{\frac{q_{x+1}}{q_x} - 1}{\frac{q_x}{q_{x-1}} - 1}$
(1)	(2)	(3)	(4)
94	.20463	1.06539	-----
95	.21801	1.06468	.98914
96	.23211	1.04735	.73208
97	.24310	1.03924	.82882
98	.25264	1.02434	.62028
99	.25879	-----	-----

We note that the test values first drop below .9 at $x=96$. Therefore 96 is the *youngest* age for which the test value is less than .9, so .23211 is retained as the value of q_{96}. The value of q_{97} is found from Equation (4.12) as

$$q_{97} = q_{96}\left[.9\left(\frac{q_{96}}{q_{95}}-1\right)+1\right] = (.23211)\left[.9(.06468)+1\right] = .24562,$$

and the value of q_{98} is similarly found as

$$q_{98} = q_{97}\left[.9\left(\frac{q_{97}}{q_{96}}-1\right)+1\right] = (.24562)\left[.9(.05821)+1\right] = .25848.$$

$\square$

4.2.4 Derivation of Other Values

Values of q_x had now been obtained for all ages 2-109 inclusive, and ℓ_0 had been taken as 100,000. For ages up to age 2, the Equation (4.9) values of $_t d_x$ were used to obtain value of ℓ_{x+t} as

$$\ell_{x+t} = \ell_x - {}_t d_x. \tag{4.13}$$

At ages 3-110, ℓ_x values were similarly derived as $\ell_{x+1} = \ell_x - d_x$ (Equation (4.2b)), where $d_x = \ell_x \cdot q_x$ (Equation (4.1b)).

Values of q_x for ages under 2 years were derived by the formulas $q_0 = 1 - \frac{\ell_1}{\ell_0}$ and $q_1 = 1 - \frac{\ell_2}{\ell_1}$, and for the several subdivisions of the first year of life,

$$_t q_x = 1 - \frac{\ell_{x+t}}{\ell_x}. \tag{4.14}$$

Values of $\overset{o}{e}_{110}$, the expectation of life at age 110 years, were furnished by the Office of the Actuary of the U.S. Social Security Administration. Given $\overset{o}{e}_{110}$ and ℓ_{110} it follows from Equation (3.7) that $T_{110} = \ell_{110} \cdot \overset{o}{e}_{110}$. Other values of T_x were calculated as

$$T_x = T_{x+1} + \tfrac{1}{2}(\ell_x + \ell_{x+1}), \tag{4.15}$$

and L_x was then found as

$$L_x = T_x - T_{x+1}. \tag{4.16}$$

Equations (4.16) and (4.15) together imply

$$L_x = \tfrac{1}{2}(\ell_x + \ell_{x+1}). \tag{4.17}$$

The remaining values of $\overset{\circ}{e}_x$ were then obtained by $\overset{\circ}{e}_x = \dfrac{T_x}{\ell_x}$.

For the subdivisions of the first year of life, the T_x formula is modified to

$$T_x = T_{x+t} + \tfrac{t}{2}(\ell_x + \ell_{x+t}), \tag{4.18}$$

using the values of t shown in the following table.

TABLE 4.2	
Age	t
0	$\dfrac{1}{365}$
1 day	$\dfrac{6}{365}$
7 days	$\dfrac{21}{365}$
28 days	$\dfrac{337}{365}$

Finally, standard errors were calculated for the life table functions q_x and $\overset{\circ}{e}_x$.[2] These errors are statements of the variability of these functions, assuming that age-specific deaths follow a binomial distribution. These error statements exclude factors such as misstatement of age, response errors, and so on.

---

[2]From a proper statistical point of view, the life table functions are just numbers, and therefore do not have variances. What is actually being calculated are the approximate variances of the *estimators* of q_x and $\overset{\circ}{e}_x$, which are random variables. The U.S. Life Tables methodology report, however, does not make this important distinction.

For ages less than 85 years, the binomial distribution assumption leads to an estimate of the variance of q_x given by

$$\sigma^2(q_x) \;=\; \frac{q_x^2(1-q_x)}{D_x^*}, \tag{4.19}$$

where D_x^* is the age-specific number of deaths, after graduation and adjustment for the number of deaths with age not stated. For ages 85-109, because of the use of the Medicare data, Equation (4.19) cannot be used. An empirical investigation led to estimates for the variances of q_x and $\overset{o}{e}_x$ at these ages.

For ages less than 85 years, the estimated variance of $\overset{o}{e}_x$ was developed as

$$\sigma^2(\overset{o}{e}_x) \;=\; \frac{\ell_{110}^2 \cdot \sigma^2(\overset{o}{e}_{110}) + \sum_{y=x}^{109} \ell_y^2 \left(\overset{o}{e}_{y+1}+\tfrac{1}{2}\right)^2 \cdot \sigma^2(q_y)}{\ell_x^2}. \tag{4.20}$$

Using the above methodology, life tables were developed for each of the 50 states, the District of Columbia, and the U.S. combined, based on 12 demographic divisions (male/female/total and white/black/other-than-white/total). In some states not all 12 tables were published if the data were too sparse. If for any racial group, fewer than 700 male or 700 female deaths at all ages were registered in the period 1979-81, then the report was not published.

In most state life tables, special adjustments were made at certain ages to correct or mitigate anomalous behavior in the life table values. This was done by redistributing by age the deaths in two or more adjacent age groups, so that the total number of deaths remained the same. A similar redistribution was not done for the national life tables.[3]

The 1979-81 U. S. Life Tables (males and females) are reproduced in Appendix B.

4.3 THE 1985-87 CANADIAN LIFE TABLES

Life tables are produced quinquennially in Canada to coincide with the quinquennial census. As with the U.S. Life Tables, deaths come from the three-year period centered on the census. Census day is June 1, 1981, 1986, and so on, rather than July 1, but the census data are used as if they were July 1 data.

---

[3]For details see "U.S. Decennial Life Tables for 1979-81, Vol. 1, No. 3," U.S. Department of Health and Human Services, May 1987.

The data used for constructing of the 1985-87 life tables included the following.

(1) The number of deaths by single years of age up to age four, and five year age groupings for ages five and over, for the years 1985, 1986, and 1987, with further subdivisions for the first year of life.
(2) The number of deaths of children up to age four, by year of birth, for the years 1985, 1986, and 1987.
(3) The census population by single years of age as of June 1, 1986.
(4) The estimated population by single years of age up to age four, for the years 1985, 1986, and 1987.
(5) The number of births by month and sex for the years 1984 to 1987.

4.3.1 Infant Tables

As was the case for the U.S. Life Tables, the infant mortality rates for the Canadian Life Tables were derived from birth and death records and did not make use of actual census population data.

For the U.S. Life Tables recall that

$$_t d_x = \ell_0 \cdot \frac{_t D_x}{_t E_x}, \tag{4.9}$$

where the exposure values denoted by the generic symbol $_t E_x$ were defined in Table 4.1. In Example 4.1 it was shown that for deaths between a and b days, for example, the exposure is

$$_t E_x = \frac{a+b}{730} B^{78} + B^{79} + B^{80} + \left(1 - \frac{a+b}{730}\right) B^{81}.$$

From there, in constructing the U.S. Life Tables up to age 2, Equations (4.13) and (4.14) were used to find ℓ_{x+t} and $_t q_x$, respectively.

By contrast, in constructing the Canadian Life Tables, data are available by month of birth, so the adjustment terms corresponding to $\frac{a+b}{730} B^{78}$ and $\left(1 - \frac{a+b}{730}\right) B^{81}$ are modified to reflect their application to a particular month. For example, for deaths at age 0-1 day,

$$_tE_x = \frac{1}{62}B^{12/84} + B^{85} + B^{86} + B^{87} - \frac{1}{62}B^{12/87}, \quad (4.21a)$$

where $B^{12/z}$ denotes the births in December of year z.
Similarly, for deaths at age 1-2 weeks,

$$_tE_x = \frac{21}{62}B^{12/84} + B^{85} + B^{86} + B^{87} - \frac{21}{62}B^{12/87}, \quad (4.21b)$$

and for deaths at age 3-4 months,

$$_tE_x = \frac{1}{2}B^{9/84} + \text{(all births in 10/84 thru 9/87)} - \frac{1}{2}B^{9/87}, (4.21c)$$

where $B^{9/z}$ denotes the births in September of year z.

Instead of then finding $_td_x$ from Equation (4.9) and $_tq_x$ from Equations (4.13) and (4.14), as was done for the U.S. tables, the Canadian method proceeds directly to the estimate of $_tq_x$, which becomes

$$_tq_x = \frac{\text{Deaths between ages } x \text{ and } x+t, \ 1985\text{-}87}{_tE_x - \text{Deaths prior to age } x, \ 1985\text{-}87}. \quad (4.22a)$$

For example, $_tq_x$ for age 1-2 days is

$$_tq_x = \frac{\text{Deaths between ages 1 and 2 days, } 1985\text{-}87}{_tE_x - \text{ Deaths under 1 day, } 1985\text{-}87}, (4.22b)$$

where $_tE_x = \frac{3}{62}B^{12/84} + B^{85} + B^{86} + B^{87} - \frac{3}{62}B^{12/87}$. Similarly, $_tq_x$ for age 1-2 weeks is

$$_tq_x = \frac{\text{Deaths between ages 1 and 2 weeks, } 1985\text{-}87}{_tE_x - \text{Deaths under 1 week, } 1985\text{-}87}, (4.22c)$$

where $_tE_x = \frac{21}{62}B^{12/84} + B^{85} + B^{86} + B^{87} - \frac{21}{62}B^{12/87}$.

The results of this analysis (by day up to 7 days, by week up to 28 days, and by month up to 1 year) are published separately as a special 1985-87 Canadian Life Table for the First Year of Life. This table is illustrated in Appendix C.

> **Example 4.4**

Given the following data, and assuming 12 months of 30 days each, show that the Canadian methodology and U.S. methodology produce the same value of $_{1\,day}q_{1\,day}$, the mortality rate for the second day of life.

$$\ell_0 = 100,000$$

$$B^{z-1} = 29,000 \text{ per month, or } 348,000 \text{ per year}$$

$$B^z = 30,000 \text{ per month, or } 360,000 \text{ per year}$$

$$B^{z+1} = 31,000 \text{ per month, or } 372,000 \text{ per year}$$

$$B^{z+2} = 32,000 \text{ per month, or } 384,000 \text{ per year}$$

$$_{1\,day}D_0 = 3500 \text{ over the observation period of calendar years } z, z+1 \text{ and } z+2$$

$$_{1\,day}D_{1\,day} = 500 \text{ over the same observation period}$$

> **Solution**

Canada:

$$_tq_x = \frac{\text{Deaths between ages } x \text{ and } x+t, z \text{ to } z+2}{_tE_x - \text{Deaths up to age } x, z \text{ to } z+2}$$

$$_{1\,day}q_{1\,day} = \frac{\text{Deaths between ages 1 and 2 days, } z \text{ to } z+2}{\frac{3}{60}B^{12/z-1}+B^z+B^{z+1}+B^{z+2}-\frac{3}{60}B^{12/z+2}-_{1\,day}D_0}$$

$$= \frac{500}{\frac{3}{60}(29,000)+1,116,000-\frac{3}{60}(32,000)-3500}$$

$$= .0004495$$

U.S.:

First we find $_{1\,day}d_0$ by using Equation (4.9), modified to reflect a year of 360 days instead of 365 days, obtaining

$$_{1\,day}d_0 \;=\; \ell_0 \, \frac{_{1\,day}D_0}{\frac{1}{720}(B^{z-1}+720B^z+720B^{z+1}+719B^{z+2})}$$

$$=\; 100,000\!\left(\frac{3500}{1,115,950}\right)$$

$$=\; 313.634.$$

Then $\ell_{1\,day} = 100,000 - 313.634 = 99,686.366$. Next we find

$$_{1\,day}d_{1\,day} \;=\; \ell_0 \, \frac{_{1\,day}D_{1\,day}}{\frac{1}{720}(3B^{z-1}+720B^z+720B^{z+1}+717B^{z+2})}$$

$$=\; 100,000\!\left(\frac{500}{1,115,850}\right)$$

$$=\; 44.809,$$

so $\ell_{2\,days} = 99,686.366 - 44.809 = 99,641.557$. Then from Equation (4.14) we find

$$_{1\,day}q_{1\,day} \;=\; 1 - \frac{\ell_{2\,days}}{\ell_{1\,day}}$$

$$=\; 1 - \frac{99,641.557}{99,686.366}$$

$$=\; .0004495.$$

Thus we find that the Canadian and U.S. methods are identical, within the modification of using a 360-day year and the assumption of an equal number of births each month.   □

4.3.2 Adult Tables

The Canadian Adult Life Tables are presented from age 0, using a derivation that is independent of that used for the Canadian Life Table for the First Year of Life. The method used to derive the adult table is different for ages 0 to 4 than for ages 5 and over.

   Deaths up to age 4 last birthday are available by year of birth. This fact allows the calculation of the values shown in the diagram on the following page.

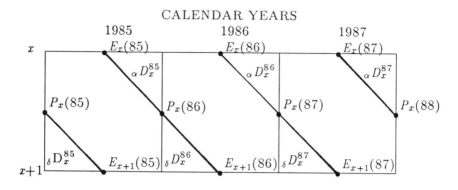

FIGURE 4.1

As illustrated in Figure 4.1, $E_x(z)$ represents the number attaining age x in calendar year z, and $P_x(z)$ represents the number living on January 1 of year z who are aged x last birthday. Because the deaths are reported by year of birth, as well as date of death, these values of $E_x(z)$ and $P_x(z)$ can be estimated from birth and infant death records. (Note that here $P_x(z)$ is an estimate of the January 1 population, whereas $P_x(z)$ in Section 4.2.2 is the April 1 census count used as an approximation to the July 1 population.) We also define $_\alpha D_x^z$ to be the number dying in year z who attained age x in year z (so that their year of birth is $z-x$), and we similarly define $_\delta D_x^z$ to be the number dying in year z who attained age x in year $z-1$ (so that their year of birth is $z-x-1$).

Recall the definition of ρ_0^z in Section 2.5 as the proportion of infant deaths in calendar year z for which the year of birth was $z-1$. Extending this definition to other ages, we see that ρ_x^z is the proportion of deaths in year z at age x last birthday for which age x was attained in year $z-1$. Then it follows that

$$_\delta D_x^z \; = \; \rho_x^z \cdot D_x^z, \qquad (4.23a)$$

$$_\alpha D_x^z \; = \; (1-\rho_x^z) \cdot D_x^z, \qquad (4.23b)$$

and

$$D_x^z \; = \; {_\alpha D_x^z} + {_\delta D_x^z}, \qquad (4.23c)$$

where D_x^z denotes all deaths in year z at age x last birthday. Note also that

$$E_x(z) - {}_\alpha D_x^z = P_x(z+1) \tag{4.24}$$

and

$$P_x(z) - {}_\delta D_x^z = E_{x+1}(z). \tag{4.25}$$

We define

$${}_\alpha p_x^z = \frac{P_x(z+1)}{E_x(z)} \tag{4.26}$$

and

$${}_\delta p_x^z = \frac{E_{x+1}(z)}{P_x(z)}, \tag{4.27}$$

which represent the probabilities of surviving the partial years. We also define

$${}_\alpha p_x^{85-87} = \frac{P_x(86) + P_x(87) + P_x(88)}{E_x(85) + E_x(86) + E_x(87)} \tag{4.28}$$

and

$${}_\delta p_x^{85-87} = \frac{E_{x+1}(85) + E_{x+1}(86) + E_{x+1}(87)}{P_x(85) + P_x(86) + P_x(87)}. \tag{4.29}$$

Then we finally have

$$p_x = {}_\alpha p_x \cdot {}_\delta p_x \tag{4.30}$$

and

$$q_x = 1 - p_x. \tag{4.31}$$

This methodology was used to derive values of q_x for ages 0 to 4 inclusive.

Quinquennially grouped data were used for ages 5 to 94, although the deaths and census populations were available by single years of age. Quinquennially grouped data has historically been used since it automatically eliminates the effects of digit preference in the reporting of ages.

Values of q_x were found for the central ages $7, 12, 17, \cdots, 92$ for age groups $(5\text{-}9), (10\text{-}14), (15\text{-}19), \cdots, (90\text{-}94)$ using the formula

$$q_x = \frac{{}_5 D_{x-2}^{85-87}}{3 \cdot {}_5 P_{x-2}(86) + \frac{1}{2} \cdot {}_5 D_{x-2}^{85-87}}. \tag{4.32}$$

(See Example 4.2 for a justification of this formula.) For example,

$$q_{17} = \frac{{}_5 D_{15}^{85-87}}{3 \cdot {}_5 P_{15}(86) + \frac{1}{2} \cdot {}_5 D_{15}^{85-87}}.$$

From these pivotal values, values for individual q_x for each integer age x from 5 to 94 were obtained using a special graduation formula.

Special formulas were also used beyond age 94 to complete the life tables. The Canadian Life Tables were terminated at age 102, so that

$$q_{102} = 1.000 \tag{4.33a}$$

and

$$\ell_{103} = 0. \tag{4.33b}$$

The provincial tables were terminated at age 85, with a final entry for all ages over 85.

Given a complete set of q_x values and a table radix of $\ell_0 = 100{,}000$, all life table columns could then be calculated as previously described. Only one departure is worth noting.

Above age 5, the value of L_x was found assuming a uniform distribution of deaths, so that

$$L_x = \frac{1}{2}(\ell_x + \ell_{x+1}). \tag{4.17}$$

The unevenness of the distribution of deaths prior to age 4, however, led the demographers to use special formulas, which were

$$L_1 = \ell_1 - (1 - f_1)d_1 \tag{4.34a}$$

and

$$L_x = \ell_x - (1 - f_x)d_x - \frac{1}{24}(d_{x-1} - d_{x+1}), \tag{4.34b}$$

for $x = 2,3,4$, where f_x is the average fraction of the year lived through by the d_x people who attain age x but die before age $x+1$

(see Example 3.3). If $f_x = \frac{1}{3}$, for example, then there are more early deaths than late deaths, and ℓ_x needs to be reduced by more than $\frac{1}{2} \cdot d_x$ to more accurately estimate the value of L_x.

The 1985-87 Canadian Life Table (male and female) are reproduced in Appendix C.

4.4 ABRIDGED LIFE TABLES

Complete life tables, listing all life table values for each age x, are not the only tables that might be produced. Life table information is commonly published in an abridged life table, showing values at age 0, age group [1-5), and then quinquennial age groups [5-10), [10-15), and so on.

Abridged life tables may be produced for two reasons. First, because of sparse data or data of questionable accuracy, it is not possible to produce a credible complete life table, as is the case for the province of Prince Edward Island, the least-populated province in Canada. Second, many users of life tables do not require the vast array of data presented in the complete life table. For them, quinquennial interval data will both suffice and greatly ease their work load and expense.

Most of the relationships in an abridged life table were defined, or follow directly from other relationships, in Chapter 3. Assuming an n-year age grouping, we would have the relationships

$$_n m_x \;=\; \frac{_n d_x}{_n L_x}, \tag{4.35a}$$

$$_n d_x \;=\; \ell_x \cdot _n q_x, \tag{4.35b}$$

$$_n d_x \;=\; \ell_x - \ell_{x+n}, \tag{4.35c}$$

$$_n L_x \;=\; \frac{n}{2}(\ell_x + \ell_{x+n}), \tag{4.35d}$$

which assumes a uniform distribution of deaths over the interval x to $x+n$, and

$$T_x \;=\; T_{x+n} + {}_nL_x. \tag{4.35e}$$

To construct an abridged life table, the demographer begins with values of ${}_nm_x$ based on observed deaths and census populations, graduated and adjusted as appropriate.

The next step is to proceed from values of ${}_nm_x$ to values of ${}_nq_x$. For age 0 and ages 1-4 (*i.e.*, q_0 and ${}_4q_1$) this is usually done with great care in a manner that varies from table to table and demographer to demographer. Methods used in the U.S. and Canada parallel those already described for the derivation of the complete life table.

For ages 5 to 85, or whatever the last entry may be in the table, mathematical formulas are usually used to proceed from ${}_nm_x$ to ${}_nq_x$. For example, assuming a uniform distribution of deaths over the quinquennial intervals we have

$$_nq_x \;=\; \frac{n \cdot {}_nm_x}{1 + \frac{n}{2} \cdot {}_nm_x}. \tag{4.36}$$

If the uniform distribution assumption is questionable, and if values of ${}_nf_x$ are available, a more accurate formula is

$$_nq_x \;=\; \frac{n \cdot {}_nm_x}{1 + n(1 - {}_nf_x){}_nm_x}. \tag{4.37}$$

Keyfitz [15] suggested an improvement to Equation (4.37). He starts with the equation

$$_nm_x \;=\; \frac{{}_nd_x}{{}_nL_x} \;=\; \frac{\int_0^n \ell_{x+t}\mu_{x+t}\,dt}{\int_0^n \ell_{x+t}\,dt},$$

and is able to show that, under assumptions given in the paper, this is the same as

$$_nm_x \;=\; \frac{1}{n}\int_0^n \mu_{x+t}\,dt + \frac{n^3}{12 \cdot {}_nL_x}\,\ell'_{x+n/2}\,\mu'_{x+n/2}, \tag{4.38}$$

where ℓ'_y and μ'_y denote the derivatives of ℓ_y and μ_y. From Equation (4.38) it follows that

$$\int_0^n \mu_{x+t}\,dt \;=\; n \cdot {}_nm_x - \frac{n^4}{12 \cdot {}_nL_x}\,\ell'_{x+n/2}\,\mu'_{x+n/2}. \tag{4.39}$$

If we then adopt the approximations

$$\ell'_{x+n/2} \approx \frac{nL_{x+n} - nL_{x-n}}{2n^2} = -\left(\frac{nL_{x-n} - nL_{x+n}}{2n^2}\right) \quad (4.40a)$$

and

$$\mu'_{x+n/2} \approx \frac{nm_{x+n} - nm_{x-n}}{2n}, \quad (4.40b)$$

and substitute them into Equation (4.39), we obtain

$$\int_0^n \mu_{x+t}\, dt = n \cdot nm_x + \frac{n}{48 \cdot nL_x}(nL_{x-n} - nL_{x+n})(nm_{x+n} - nm_{x-n}).$$

Since

$$nq_x = 1 - exp\left(-\int_0^n \mu_{x+t}\, dt\right),$$

then we find

$$nq_x = 1 - exp\left(-n \cdot nm_x - \frac{n}{48 \cdot nL_x}(nL_{x-n} - nL_{x+n})(nm_{x+n} - nm_{x-n})\right),$$
$$(4.41)$$

which is known as Keyfitz' formula.

Alternatively if we substitute the identity

$$\ell'_{x+n/2} = -\ell_{x+n/2}\,\mu_{x+n/2}$$

into Equation (4.38), and rearrange, we obtain

$$\int_0^n \mu_{x+t}\, dt = n \cdot nm_x + \frac{n^4}{12 \cdot nL_x}\ell_{x+n/2}\,\mu_{x+n/2}\,\mu'_{x+n/2}. \quad (4.42)$$

If we then adopt the approximations

$$\ell_{x+n/2} \approx \tfrac{1}{n} \cdot nL_x \quad (4.43a)$$

and

$$\mu_{x+n/2} \approx nm_x, \quad (4.43b)$$

and substitute them into Equation (4.42), we obtain

$$\int_0^n \mu_{x+t}\, dt = n \cdot {}_n m_x + \frac{n^3}{12} \cdot {}_n m_x \cdot {}_n m_x'$$

$$= n \cdot {}_n m_x + \frac{n^3}{12} \cdot {}_n m_x{}^2 (\ln {}_n m_x)', \qquad (4.44)$$

which is known as Greville's formula (see Keyfitz and Smith [18], pp. 53-60).

Based on the analysis of several life tables, Greville found that $(\ln {}_n m_x)'$ was nearly constant and close to .096. Then Equation (4.44) becomes

$$\int_0^n \mu_{x+t}\, dt = n \cdot {}_n m_x + \frac{n^3}{12}({}_n m_x{}^2)(.096)$$

$$= n \cdot {}_n m_x + .008 n^3 \cdot {}_n m_x{}^2,$$

which leads to

$${}_n q_x = 1 - {}_n p_x = 1 - exp\left(-\int_0^n \mu_{x+t}\, dt\right)$$

$$= 1 - exp\left(-n \cdot {}_n m_x - .008 n^3 \cdot {}_n m_x{}^2\right). \qquad (4.45a)$$

This is known as the Reed-Merrell formula, derived empirically by Reed and Merrell in 1939 (see Keyfitz and Smith [18], pp. 43-49). Since $n=5$ in most abridged life tables, we have

$${}_5 q_x = 1 - exp\left[-{}_5 m_x(5 + {}_5 m_x)\right] \qquad (4.45b)$$

for the Reed-Merrell formula.

As has been stated, formulas such as Equations (4.36) through (4.45) are normally used only up to an upper bound such as age 85, with values beyond age 85 presented as a final age group. Since ${}_n m_x = \frac{{}_n d_x}{{}_n L_x}$ and $\ell_x = \sum_{t=0}^{\infty} d_{x+t}$, then for the final age group ${}_\infty m_x = \frac{{}_\infty d_x}{{}_\infty L_x} = \frac{\ell_x}{{}_\infty L_x}$. This is used to derive the terminal values ${}_\infty L_x = \frac{\ell_x}{{}_\infty m_x}$ and $T_x = {}_\infty L_x$.

Example 4.5

Given the following life table values, determine $_5q_{50}$ using each of the following methods.

x	$_5m_x$	$_5L_x$
45	.0025654	479,463
50	.0040983	471,659
55	.0063195	459,686

(a) Uniform distribution of deaths over the age interval 50 to 55
(b) Constant force of mortality between ages 50 and 55
(c) Keyfitz' formula
(d) The Reed-Merrell formula

Solution

(a) Extending Equation (4.8) we have

$$_5q_{50} = \frac{5 \cdot {}_5m_{50}}{1 + \frac{5}{2} \cdot {}_5m_{50}} = .0202836.$$

(b) From Examples 3.12 and 3.13 we know that $q_x = 1 - e^{-m_x}$. Over an n-year interval this extends to $_nq_x = 1 - exp(-n \cdot {}_nm_x)$. Then

$$_5q_{50} = 1 - exp(-5 \cdot {}_5m_x) = .0202829.$$

(c) Using Equation (4.41), we have

$$_5q_{50} = 1 - exp\left(-5 \cdot {}_5m_{50} - \frac{5}{48 \cdot {}_5L_{50}}({}_5L_{45} - {}_5L_{55})({}_5m_{55} - {}_5m_{45})\right)$$

$$= 1 - e^{-.0204915 - .0000164}$$

$$= .0202990.$$

(d) Using Equation (4.45a) we have

$$_5q_{50} = 1 - exp\left(-5 \cdot {}_5m_{50} - .008(5)^3 \cdot {}_5m_{50}{}^2\right)$$

$$= 1 - e^{-.0205082}$$

$$= .0202994. \qquad \square$$

4.5 ANALYSIS OF THE LIFE TABLE BY CAUSE OF DEATH

For jurisdictions that are able to determine the cause of death on all death certificates, it is possible to divide the life table into components according to specific causes of death. We can then present data that could be used, for example, to calculate the probability of ultimately dying from any of the specified causes, or to calculate the increase in the expectation of life that would result by completely eliminating any one cause of death.

Define the proportion of observed deaths in the age interval x to $x+n$ resulting from cause i to be

$$_n r_x^i \;=\; \frac{_n D_x^i}{_n D_x}. \tag{4.46}$$

If we then assume that the same ratio by cause can be applied to the $_n d_x$ column in the associated life table, we have

$$_n d_x^i \;=\; _n r_x^i \cdot _n d_x \tag{4.47}$$

for the number of deaths between x and $x+n$ resulting from cause i. We can then calculate cause-specific life tables whereby

$$\ell_x^i \;=\; \sum_x {_n d_x^i}, \tag{4.48}$$

so that the probability of ultimately dying from cause i is $\frac{\ell_x^i}{\ell_x}$. Next we define

$$_n r_x^{(-i)} \;=\; 1 - {_n r_x^i} \tag{4.49}$$

to be the proportion of observed deaths from all causes other than cause i. It can now be shown that the probability of surviving from age x to age $x+n$ if cause i can be eliminated is

$$_n p_x^{(-i)} \;=\; \left(_n p_x\right)^{(1 - _n r_x^i)}. \tag{4.50}$$

| Example 4.6 |

Prove Equation (4.50), under the assumption that the ratio $\frac{\mu_y^i}{\mu_y}$ is constant over the interval x to $x+n$, where μ_y^i denotes the force of mortality at age y due to cause i.

Solution

Let $\frac{\mu_y^i}{\mu_y} = k$, so that $\mu_y^i = k \cdot \mu_y$. Then

$$_n r_x^i = \frac{_n d_x^i}{_n d_x} = \frac{\int_0^n \ell_{x+t} \mu_{x+t}^i \, dt}{\int_0^n \ell_{x+t} \mu_{x+t} \, dt} = \frac{\int_0^n \ell_{x+t} \cdot k \cdot \mu_{x+t} \, dt}{\int_0^n \ell_{x+t} \mu_{x+t} \, dt} = k,$$

so that $\mu_y^i = {_n r_x^i} \cdot \mu_y$. Next we note that $\mu_{x+t}^i + \mu_{x+t}^{(-i)} = \mu_{x+t}$, so

$$\mu_{x+t}^{(-i)} = \mu_{x+t} - \mu_{x+t}^i = (1 - {_n r_x^i}) \mu_{x+t}.$$

This leads to

$$exp\left(-\int_0^n \mu_{x+t}^{(-i)} \, dt \right) = exp\left(-\int_0^n (1 - {_n r_x^i}) \mu_{x+t} \, dt \right)$$

or

$$_n p_x^{(-i)} = ({_n p_x})^{(1 - {_n r_x^i})}. \qquad\qquad \square$$

From this point, for the life table from which cause of death i has been eliminated, we have

$$\ell_{x+n}^{(-i)} = \ell_x^{(-i)} \cdot {_n p_x^{(-i)}} \qquad\qquad (4.51a)$$

and

$$_n d_x^{(-i)} = \ell_x^{(-i)} - \ell_{x+n}^{(-i)}, \qquad\qquad (4.51b)$$

which are used recursively until the entire table is constructed. From definitions and formulas already presented, we can find the value of $\overset{o}{e}_x^{(-i)}$, the expectation of life after cause i has been eliminated. The gain in the expectation of life by eliminating cause of death i is therefore $\overset{o}{e}_x^{(-i)} - \overset{o}{e}_x$.

4.6 EXERCISES

4.1 Introduction;   4.2 The 1979-81 U.S. Life Tables

4-1. Consider the following data.

Year	Births	Number of Deaths Between Exact Ages			
		0-1 day $[0, 1)$	1-7 days $[1, 7)$	7-28 days $[7, 28)$	28-365 days $[28, 365)$
1977	700	---	---	---	---
1978	750	---	---	---	---
1979	800	14	20	12	30
1980	850	12	24	13	27
1981	900	18	29	11	33

Use the methodology of the 1979-81 U.S. Life Tables and the radix $\ell_0 = 100{,}000$ to find ℓ_x for $x = \frac{1}{365}, \frac{7}{365}, \frac{28}{365}$, and 1.

4-2. Consider the following data.

x	$P_x(80)$	D_x^{79-81}
2	2500	5
3	2490	7
4	2480	6

Estimate q_3 using the methodology of the 1979-81 U.S. Life Tables.

4-3. Given the following estimates based on census and Medicare data, determine q_{90} using the methodology of the 1979-81 U.S. Life Tables.

x	q_x^C	q_x^M
90	.190	.185

4-4. Consider the following data.

Year	Births	Deaths at Age 1	
1977	4,000,000	--	
1978	3,900,000	--	
1979	3,800,000	20,000	$\ell_0 = 100,000$
1980	3,700,000	19,000	$\ell_1 = 99,000$
1981	3,600,000	18,500	

Determine q_1 using the methodology of the 1979-81 U.S. Life Tables.

4-5. In constructing the 1979-81 U.S. Life Tables, the following q_x values were produced from Medicare data.

x	q_x
92	.16175
93	.17624
94	.19092
95	.20524
96	.21868
97	.23063

Find the value of q_{96} actually used in the final version of the U.S. Life Table.

4-6. Find $\overset{o}{e}_{107}$ using the methodology of the 1979-81 U.S. Life Tables, given the following values.

$\ell_{107} = 13,000$ $\ell_{109} = 7,000$ $\overset{o}{e}_{110} = 2.20$
$\ell_{108} = 10,000$ $\ell_{110} = 5,000$

4.3 The 1985-87 Canadian Life Tables

4-7. Given the following data, find q_1^{86} using the method of the Canadian Adult Life Tables.

$P_1(86) = 50,000$ $P_1(87) = 59,700$

$E_1(86) = 60,000$ $E_2(86) = 49,800$

4-8.   The records for a certain community give the following data.

Calendar Year of Birth   1986   1987
No. Living January 1, 1988   26,000   28,000

Death Records: $D_0^{88} = 300$

$$D_1^{88} = 120$$

$$D_0^{89} = 320$$

$$D_1^{89} = 130$$

Assuming no migration and that $\rho_0^z = .3$ and $\rho_1^z = .4$ for all z, find each of the following.

(a) $E_2(88)$ (b) $P_1(89)$

(c) q_1^{88}, using the method of the Canadian Adult Life Tables

4-9.   The records of a community contain the death and population data shown below. A separate study showns that 70% of those who died at age 0, 60% of those who died at age 1, and 50% of those who died at age 2 had their last birthday in the same calendar year as that in which death occurred.

Age Last Birthday	Number of Deaths				Population as of December 31		
	1986	1987	1988	1989	1986	1987	1988
0	3000	3200	3500	3900	25,000	25,900	27,000
1		800	900	1000	22,750	23,560	24,310
2			300	400			

Calculate each of the following.

(a) The number born in 1987
(b) The number attaining age 1 in 1987
(c) The number alive on December 31, 1988 who are age 2 last birthday
(d) q_1^{88}, using the method of the Canadian Adult Life Tables

4-10. Consider the following information.

Deaths During Quarter of Life	Calendar Year 1989	1990	Births During Calendar Quarter	Calendar Year 1989	1990
1st	4	10	1st	100	90
2nd	4	6	2nd	60	70
3rd	6	8	3rd	90	70
4th	5	3	4th	80	110

Approximate the probability of death in the second quarter of life in 1990, assuming a uniform distribution of deaths and births.

4-11. Consider the following information, and assume an even distribution of birthdays and no migration.

	1988	1989	1990
Births	5275	5237	7210
Deaths Age 0	200	210	300
Age 1	100	120	210
ρ_0^z	.3	.3	.3
ρ_1^z	.4	.4	.4

Find each of the following values, using the methodology of the Canadian Adult Life Tables.

(a) $E_1(90)$ 　　　　 (b) $_\alpha D_1^{89}$ 　　　　 (c) q_1^{90}

4-12. Use the methodology of the Canadian Infant Life Tables to estimate $_{1/52}q_{1/52}$, the probability of dying during the second week of life, given the following information.

Year z	Births in Year z	Births in December, z	Deaths in 1st week of life	Deaths in 2nd week of life
1984	378,000	33,000	1,735	160
1985	377,000	32,000	1,730	164
1986	376,000	31,000	1,725	159
1987	375,000	30,000	1,720	157

4-13. Use the methodology of the Canadian Adult Life Tables to estimate q_2^{85-87}, given the following information.

Year z	$P_2(z)$	$_\alpha D_2^z$	$_\delta D_2^z$
1985	350,000	321	330
1986	352,000	319	332
1987	354,000	326	340
1988	356,000		

4-14. Find the value of f_2 used in constructing the 1985-87 Canadian Female Adult Life Table, shown in Appendix C.

4-15. Find $\overset{o}{e}_{51}$, given the following information and assuming a uniform distribution of deaths.

$$\ell_{50} = 204$$

$$\ell_{51} = 200$$

$$\overset{o}{e}_{50} = 30.52$$

4.4 Abridged Life Tables

4-16. Given that $_5m_{40} = .02$, find $_5q_{40}$ using each of the following approaches.

(a) Uniform distribution of deaths over the interval 40 to 45
(b) The Reed-Merrell formula

4-17. An abridged life table is being constructed using the Reed-Merrell formula. If $_nm_{70} = .12$ and $_nq_{70} = .585$, find the integral value of n.

4-18. Estimate $\overset{o}{e}_0$ and $\overset{o}{e}_{10}$, given the values $_{10}m_0 = .002$ and $_\infty m_{10} = .020$.

4.5 Analysis of the Life Table by Cause of Death

4-19. In a certain community with a population of 125,000 between ages 50 and 55, there were 625 deaths from all causes between those ages, of which 125 were due to cancer.

(a) Find $_5q_{50}$ assuming a uniform distribution of deaths.

(b) Estimate $_5q_{50}^{(-i)}$ if cancer is eliminated as a cause of death.

4-20. The following information is available for a certain community.

Age Last Birthday x	ℓ_x	$\overset{o}{e}_x$	Percent of Deaths Due to Cancer Between Age x and Age $x+50$
0	100	70	10
50	85	30	40
100	0	0	

Assuming that $\mu_y^{(-c)} = {}_nr_x^{(-c)} \cdot \mu_y$, for $x \leq y \leq x+n$, and ${}_nm_x^{(-c)} = {}_nr_x^{(-c)} \cdot {}_nm_x$, find each of the following.

(a) $_{50}m_0$ (b) $_{50}p_0^{(-c)}$ (c) $\overset{o}{e}_{50}^{(-c)}$ (d) $\overset{o}{e}_0^{(-c)}$

4-21. In a given population, $_{10}r_{40}^a = \frac{1}{8}$ and $_{10}r_{40}^b = \frac{1}{10}$, where a and b are two important causes of death. Estimate the value of $\dfrac{\log_e {}_{10}p_{40}^{(-a)}}{\log_e {}_{10}p_{40}^{(-b)}}$.

4-22. Given that $_{10}p_{30} = .8$ and 750 out of 1000 deaths between ages 30 and 40 are due to malaria, find $_{10}p_{30}^{(-i)}$ if malaria is eliminated as a cause of death.

CHAPTER 5

STATIONARY POPULATION THEORY

5.1 INTRODUCTION

A major area of demographic work is that of *population analysis*, including population projections. As a population evolves over time it is augmented by new births, diminished by deaths, and either augmented or diminished by net immigration or net emigration, as the case may be. The formal population analysis presented in this text is confined to the elements of births and deaths only, with migration considered in a more informal (*i.e.*, non-mathematical) manner.

Setting aside migration then, the characteristics of a population, including its projected future size and age distribution, are functions of the birth and death patterns operating in that population. Note that analogues for birth and death are fertility and mortality, respectively. Thus we will frequently speak of the set of fertility and mortality rates, or the fertility and mortality *profiles*, that operate in a certain population.

The concept of fertility rates, including those that are age-and-sex-specific, was defined in Chapter 2, along with the standard demographic approach for quantifying, or estimating, such rates from census and vital statistics data. Similarly, the concept of a mortality profile, in the traditional form of a life table, was described in detail in Chapter 3. Various approaches to quantifying, or estimating, the life table values from population data were explored in Chapter 4.

With a good understanding of the important fertility and mortality models in hand, we are now ready to begin our study of population analysis, a topic that will occupy the next three chapters of the text. We will consider four examples of population analysis.

We will begin with the simplest example, which is the analysis of a single group of births. Since this is a *closed group* of newborn lives, no fertility model comes into play. Since immigration is not being considered, the analysis of this birth group is a function of the applicable mortality profile (*i.e.*, life table) only. We will refer to this example as an *analysis of the survivorship group*; it is presented in Section 5.2 of this chapter.

Our second example will be that of the *stationary population*, presented in the remaining sections of this chapter. This example differs from the first in that several consecutive annual birth groups are considered. The annual number of births is assumed to be constant over time, and the same mortality profile is assumed to apply to all birth groups. Because of the number of births is fixed, it is again the case that no fertility model applies, and the characteristics of the population are functions of the mortality model only.

In Chapter 6 we generalize the stationary population model to allow for a changing birth pattern over time, so that an assumed fertility profile is incorporated into the model along with the assumed mortality profile, which is still assumed to apply unchanged to successive birth groups over time. This model is called a *stable population*. A more general case, called a *quasi-stable population* and presented in Section 6.5, relaxes the assumption of a constant mortality profile over time.

Finally, in Chapter 7, we consider population projections in a more general setting, again making use of assumed fertility and mortality profiles.

5.2 ANALYSIS OF THE SURVIVORSHIP GROUP

Consider a group of newborn lives of size B, and a life table that is assumed to apply to those B newborn lives. As a preliminary step, we need to be very specific as to what we mean by saying that the life table "applies" to this group.

In our introduction to Chapter 3, we mentioned that a life table model can be viewed in either a stochastic or a deterministic framework. In the former view, a model applies to a group of people in a probabilistic sense. Thus if we have a group of ℓ_x

people exactly age x, we would say that $\ell_{x+n} = \ell_x \cdot {}_np_x$ is the *expected* number, out of the ℓ_x group, that will survive to age $x+n$.

The deterministic view is simpler, and, accordingly, somewhat more restrictive. In this view we merely say that ℓ_{x+n} of the ℓ_x people *do survive* to age $x+n$. Although the life table really is a predictive (*i.e.*, probabilistic) model, we agree to ignore that for the moment and act as if the story it tells about its ℓ_0 birth group represents the pattern that a group of births actually follows. In this chapter we take a totally deterministic view of the mortality profile model given by the adopted life table.

Suppose, for convenience, that the size of our group of newborn lives is $B = \ell_0$, where the numerical value of this ℓ_0 is exactly the same as the ℓ_0 radix value of the adopted life table. Then we can describe the progression of our survivorship group in terms of values taken directly from the life table. For example, the number of persons surviving to any future age y is *precisely* the value of ℓ_y given by the life table. Similarly, the number who die between ages y and $y+n$ is *precisely* the value of $\ell_y - \ell_{y+n}$ given by the life table. The total future lifetime of the ℓ_x survivors to age x is *precisely* T_x life-years, where T_x is the life table value defined in Chapter 3. It is in this sense that the adopted life table applies to our survivorship group.

If the size of our group of newborns, B, is not exactly equal to the ℓ_0 value of the life table, we simply adjust the table values proportionally to obtain answers to questions about our group. Thus the number of survivors to age y is not the ℓ_y value from the life table, but rather is $\ell_y \cdot \dfrac{B}{\ell_0}$, where the table's ℓ_y value is adjusted in the proportion that our birth group bears to the radix (*i.e.*, the "birth group") of the life table. Because it is so easy to adjust for cases where $B \neq \ell_0$, we will do all our analysis in this chapter assuming $B = \ell_0$ without loss of generality. Many cases with $B \neq \ell_0$ will be illustrated in the examples and exercises.

So far we have merely spoken of ℓ_0 newborn lives, without saying *when* they were born, so this group of births was somewhat abstract. To carry the analysis further, and to lay the groundwork for expanding the analysis to the stationary population model in the following section, let us now make the further assumption that our ℓ_0 births occur over a one-year period, and do so uniformly over that period. Let us also assume that the same mortality profile (*i.e.*, life table) applies to each birth, regardless of when within the year that birth occurred.

This pair of assumptions, that births are evenly distributed over time and that the same mortality applies to all births, has a valuable implication. Recall that ℓ_0 births implies ℓ_x persons surviving to age x. The even distribution of births assumption implies that in any fraction of a year of length h there will be $h \cdot \ell_0$ births, which in turn produces $h \cdot \ell_x$ persons surviving to age x. Since the same deterministic mortality profile applies to *any* $h \cdot \ell_0$ group of births, then all of them lead to the same number of survivors at age x, $h \cdot \ell_x$. Since h can be made arbitrarily small, this shows that the ℓ_x persons reaching age x in a year do so uniformly over that year. This very important concept is illustrated in the following figure.

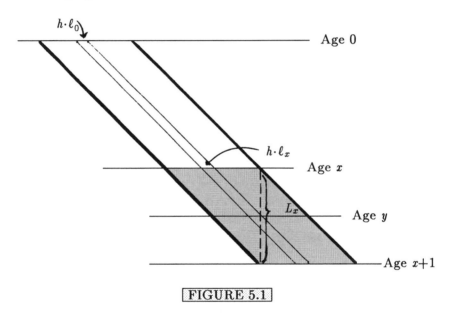

FIGURE 5.1

In Chapter 3 we defined the function L_x to be the number of life-years lived by the ℓ_x people over the year of age from x to $x+1$. This could be described as the number of life-years lived in the shaded parallelogram of Figure 5.1. Then with the definition of T_x as

$$T_x = L_x + L_{x+1} + \cdots, \qquad (5.1)$$

we see that T_x is the total future lifetime of the ℓ_x group, as already mentioned in Chapter 3. This in turn leads to

$$\overset{\circ}{e}_x = \frac{T_x}{\ell_x} \tag{5.2}$$

as the average future lifetime, or complete expectation of life, for the ℓ_x group, and

$$x + \overset{\circ}{e}_x = x + \frac{T_x}{\ell_x} \tag{5.3}$$

as the average age at death for this group.

Analogous to the complete expectation of life defined by (5.2) is a measure called the *curtate expectation of life*, denoted by e_x, in which only complete years of life are included. Since only ℓ_{x+1} *complete* years are lived between ages x and $x+1$ (one year for each of the ℓ_{x+1} survivors), ℓ_{x+2} complete years are lived between ages $x+1$ and $x+2$, and so on, then we see that the total future number of complete years lived by the ℓ_x group is $\sum_{t=1}^{\infty} \ell_{x+t}$. The curtate expectation of life is the average number of complete future years of life, so

$$e_x = \frac{1}{\ell_x} \sum_{t=1}^{\infty} \ell_{x+t} = \sum_{t=1}^{\infty} {}_t p_x. \tag{5.4}$$

Example 5.1

Show that, under the uniform distribution of deaths assumption, $\overset{\circ}{e}_x = e_x + \frac{1}{2}$.

Solution

From Example 3.9 we have $L_x = \ell_x - \frac{1}{2} \cdot d_x = \ell_{x+1} + \frac{1}{2} \cdot d_x$. Then we have

$$\overset{\circ}{e}_x = \frac{T_x}{\ell_x} = \frac{1}{\ell_x} \sum_{t=0}^{\infty} L_{x+t}$$

$$= \frac{1}{\ell_x} \sum_{t=0}^{\infty} \left(\ell_{x+t+1} + \frac{1}{2} \cdot d_{x+t} \right)$$

$$= \frac{1}{\ell_x} \left(\sum_{t=1}^{\infty} \ell_{x+t} + \frac{1}{2} \cdot \sum_{t=0}^{\infty} d_{x+t} \right)$$

$$= e_x + \frac{1}{2},$$

since $\sum_{t=0}^{\infty} d_{x+t} = \ell_x$. $\qquad\qquad\square$

Example 5.2

Use an integral expression to derive the average age at death for the people who survive to age x, as given by Equation (5.3).

Solution

The number of persons in this group is ℓ_x. The total number of life-years lived by this group in the future is $\int_x^\infty y \cdot \ell_y \mu_y \, dy$. ($\ell_y$ persons survive to age y, and $\ell_y \mu_y \, dy$ is the differential number of deaths at age y, so $y \cdot \ell_y \mu_y \, dy$ is the total of the ages at death of those who die at age y.) Using integration by parts we obtain

$$-y \cdot \ell_y \Big|_x^\infty + \int_x^\infty \ell_y \, dy = x \cdot \ell_x + T_x,$$

so the average age is $x + \dfrac{T_x}{\ell_x}$, which is Equation (5.3). □

Example 5.3

Find the average age at death for those who die between ages x and $x+n$.

Solution

The number of persons in this group is

$$\int_x^{x+n} \ell_y \mu_y \, dy = \ell_x - \ell_{x+n}.$$

The total number of life years lived by the group is $\int_x^{x+n} y \cdot \ell_y \mu_y \, dy$, which is evaluated using integration by parts to obtain

$$-y \cdot \ell_y - T_y \Big|_x^{x+n} = -(x+n)\ell_{x+n} - T_{x+n} + x \cdot \ell_x + T_x.$$

When divided by the number of deaths, which is $\ell_x - \ell_{x+n}$, we obtain $x + \dfrac{T_x - T_{x+n} - n \cdot \ell_{x+n}}{\ell_x - \ell_{x+n}}$ for the average age at death. □

One more important concept needs to be developed with regard to our survivorship group of ℓ_0 births. Referring to Figure 5.1, recall that there are $h \cdot \ell_0$ births in a fraction of a year of size h, from which $h \cdot \ell_y$ persons survive to age y. Since h can be made arbitrarily small, we let $h = dy$ and observe that $\ell_0 \, dy$ births give rise to $\ell_y \, dy$ persons turning age y over an infinitesimal interval of length dy. If we interpret the vertical broken line in Figure 5.1 as a point in time, then we can say that $\ell_y \, dy$ represents the differential number of persons who are precisely age y at that point in time.

Finally, integrating $\ell_y \, dy$ between x and $x+1$ we obtain the total number of persons in the survivorship group at that time. Then we have

$$L_x \;=\; \int_x^{x+1} \ell_y \, dy, \tag{5.5}$$

which is the same as Equation (3.9).

Thus we see that L_x has two different meanings: it represents the complete number of life-years lived between ages x and $x+1$, and it also represents the number of people alive in the survivorship group when they are all between ages x and $x+1$. Figure 5.1 shows that the point of time when this occurs is exactly $x+1$ years after the start of the year (or x years after the end of the year) in which the ℓ_0 births occurred. It is important to recognize that the first meaning of L_x holds for *any* group of ℓ_0 births, whereas the second meaning is a consequence of the pair of assumptions as to the births occurring uniformly over a year and mortality being constant over time. The second meaning of L_x will lead to a second meaning of T_x, as we will see in the next section.

5.3 THE STATIONARY POPULATION

The *stationary population* model is a simple extension of the ideas developed in the previous section, in which we had a group of ℓ_0 births, occurring evenly over a year, and a mortality profile (given by a life table) that applied to all births in this group. We now extend the model by assuming ℓ_0 births *every year*, evenly distributed over that year, and assuming that the same life table applies to all births over time. The properties of a population for which these two assumptions hold are natural extensions of the properties of the survivorship group presented in Section 5.2.

The fundamental property of the population is that of *stationarity*, by which we mean that all demographic characteristics of the population, and of any subset of the population, remain the same over time. This result is an intuitive consequence of the assumptions of constant number of births and constant mortality over time, and can be mathematically demonstrated as well.

For the moment let us assume there is no migration into the population (other than by birth) and no migration out (other than by death). We will see later that migration can be incorporated into the model very easily. Figure 5.2 illustrates the status of the population at the point of time represented by the broken vertical line.

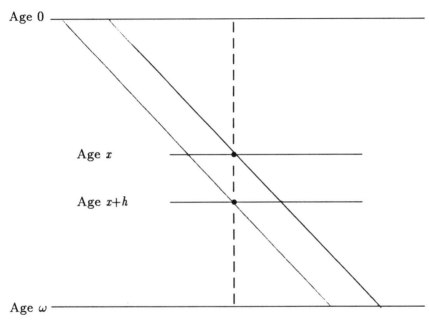

Age 0

Age x

Age $x+h$

Age ω

$\boxed{\text{FIGURE 5.2}}$

At the given point of time, there will be $_hL_x$ people in the population between ages x and $x+h$, as the survivors of the illustrated birth group of size $h\cdot\ell_0$. At *any other* point of time, the persons then between x and $x+h$ will be the survivors of a different birth group. But since both birth groups are of the same size, and both birth groups experience the same mortality, then the $_hL_x$ people alive between x and $x+h$ at the two different time points will be the same size group. Since the choice of h is arbitrary, it follows that the age composition of the population is stationary over time.

If $h = 1$ we have L_0 people alive between ages 0 and 1 at any time, L_1 people alive between ages 1 and 2 at any time, and so on. By Equation (5.1) this means the total population is of size T_0

at any time. More generally we can say that the population that is aged x and over is of size T_x at any time.

At any age y we have ℓ_y people reaching age y *in a year*, as the survivors of the ℓ_0 births occurring y years earlier. The differential number of deaths at age y in a year is $\ell_y \mu_y\, dy$, so the total number of deaths in a year in the entire population is the integral of $\ell_y \mu_y\, dy$ over all ages. Thus we have

$$D = \int_0^\omega \ell_y \mu_y\, dy, \qquad (5.6)$$

which evaluates to $D = \ell_0$. This is an expected result, since clearly there must be as many exits from the population (through death) as there are entrants (through birth) in order to maintain stationarity.

This result can be generalized to a fraction h of a year. The birth group $h\cdot\ell_0$ leads to $h\cdot\ell_y$ survivors at age y, and $h\cdot\ell_y \mu_y\, dy$ deaths at age y in a fraction h of a year. Clearly $h\cdot\ell_y \mu_y\, dy$ integrates over all ages to $h\cdot\ell_0$, so we see there is an equal number of births and deaths in *any* fraction of a year, however small. This demonstrates that the stationary property holds in a continuous manner, and not just over a finite interval such as one year.

Example 5.4

Show that there are ℓ_x deaths in a stationary population in a year at ages x and over.

Solution

This follows directly from Equation (5.6). The annual deaths at ages x and over is given by

$$\int_x^\omega \ell_y \mu_y\, dy = -\ell_y \Big|_x^\omega = \ell_x,$$

as expected. In order that the subpopulation over age x remains stationary, there must be as many people leaving it through death in a year as there are entering it through the attainment of age x. □

To summarize, then, we have established the property of stationarity for our population, and we have established the two functions ℓ_x and T_x, each with two different meanings: ℓ_x is the number of people attaining age x in a year, as well as the number of deaths in a year at ages x and over; T_x is the number of people in the population at ages x and over at any time, as well as the total future lifetime of any ℓ_x group.

A third important function required for stationary population analysis is Y_x, defined as

$$Y_x = \int_x^\omega T_y \, dy. \tag{5.7}$$

Recall that ℓ_y people have a total future lifetime of T_y, so that $\ell_y \, dy$ people have a total future lifetime of $T_y \, dy$. Integrating over all y from age x to age ω, we obtain the total future lifetime of all people who are aged x and over, which is T_x such people. Thus we have a meaning for Y_x as the total future lifetime of the T_x people aged x and over. As a special case, Y_0 is the total future lifetime of the entire population, since the total population is of size T_0. In Example 5.6 we will find a second meaning for Y_x.

Two minor issues remain to be discussed. As we saw in Section 5.2, if the constant annual birth group is of size B rather than ℓ_0, then all quantities in the stationary population will be in the proportion $\frac{B}{\ell_0}$ to what they would have been if there had been ℓ_0 annual births. This is a minor adjustment to make in any stationary population analysis, and is illustrated several times in the examples and exercises that follow.

The second issue concerns the presence of migration into or out of the population other than by birth or death. As long as such migration is consistent over time, the property of stationarity is retained. For example, suppose 50% of the people reaching age 65 migrate out of the population (by moving to a retirement climate, for example). Then the subpopulation over age 65 is supplied by only $.50\ell_{65}$ people each year, rather than ℓ_{65} as would have been the case in absence of migration. This means that the over-65 population is of size $.50T_{65}$ (rather than T_{65}), and their total future lifetime is $.50Y_{65}$ (rather than Y_{65}). Of course there would be $.50\ell_{65}$ annual deaths at ages 65 and over, rather than ℓ_{65}. Adjustments for migration are easy to make; these adjustments are illustrated in Example 5.5 and others to follow.

With the three basic functions ℓ_x, T_x, and Y_x defined (along with the additional function $L_x = T_x - T_{x+1}$), we are ready to develop answers to various questions about stationary populations. This is pursued for the remainder of this chapter through worked examples. In these examples, any numerical solutions have been obtained by evaluating the population symbols from the 1985-87 Canadian Life Tables (Male) provided in Appendix C.

| Example 5.5 |

A peacetime army is maintained by 400,000 annual inductees who are drafted on their 21st birthday. Sixty percent of the survivors are discharged on their 23rd birthday and the remainder on their 25th birthday. Determine the size of the mature army, after it has been in existence for at least four years, the number of soldiers who die each year, and the number discharged each year.

| Solution |

This example illustrates several variations on the basic stationary population model: entry occurs other than by birth at age 0, departure is by migration as well as by death, and since the number of entrants is not precisely ℓ_{21}, the proportionalizing step is required. Note that this army meets all the requirements of a stationary population outlined earlier, with the constant number of entrants at age 21. Since the population spans only a four-year age range, it will be stationary if the conditions have held for the past four years. If the number of entrants were equal to the ℓ_{21} value from the applicable life table, then the size of the mature army would be

$$L_{21} + L_{22} + .4L_{23} + .4L_{24} = (T_{21} - .6T_{23} - .4T_{25}).$$

Since the actual number of entrants is 400,000 rather than ℓ_{21}, the actual size will be

$$\frac{400,000}{\ell_{21}} (T_{21} - .6T_{23} - .4T_{25}) = 1,117,594.$$

The number of soldiers who die while in the army each year is

$$\frac{400,000}{\ell_{21}} (d_{21} + d_{22} + .4d_{23} + .4d_{24}) = \frac{400,000}{\ell_{21}} (\ell_{21} - .6\ell_{23} - .4\ell_{25}) = 1535.$$

The number of soldiers discharged each year will be

$$\frac{400,000}{\ell_{21}} (.6\ell_{23} + .4\ell_{25}) = 398,465.$$

Note that the total number leaving the army each year, either by death or discharge, exactly equals the number of inductees. This must be the case if the army is to be modeled as a stationary population, since other immigration is not allowed. □

Example 5.6

Find the total past lifetime and the total lifetime for the T_x people aged x and over.

Solution

Clearly these people are all alive today at ages x and over, so their total past lifetime *prior to age x* is $x \cdot T_x$. This population will also have past lifetime after age x since its members are of ages x and over. For the $\ell_y \, dy$ people attaining age y at any moment, their past lifetime after age x is $(y-x)\ell_y \, dy$ years. Thus the total past lifetime after age x for the entire T_x group is $\int_x^\infty (y-x)\ell_y \, dy$, which is evaluated using integration by parts to obtain

$$- y \cdot T_y - Y_y + x \cdot T_y \big|_x^\infty = x \cdot T_x + Y_x - x \cdot T_x = Y_x.$$

Therefore Y_x represents, in a stationary population, both the *total future lifetime* for the T_x people aged x and over as well as their *total past lifetime since age x*. Thus for the T_x people now alive aged x and over, we have the following results.

$$\text{Total past lifetime before age } x: \quad x \cdot T_x$$

$$\text{Total past lifetime after age } x: \quad Y_x$$

$$\text{Total past lifetime:} \quad x \cdot T_x + Y_x$$

$$\text{Total future lifetime:} \quad Y_x$$

$$\text{Total lifetime:} \quad x \cdot T_x + 2 Y_x \qquad \qquad \square$$

Example 5.7

Find the total past lifetime for those now alive aged 40 to 65.

Solution

This is given by $\int_{40}^{65} y \cdot \ell_y \, dy$. Using integration by parts we find

$$-y \cdot T_y \big|_{40}^{65} + \int_{40}^{65} T_y \, dy = -y \cdot T_y - Y_y \bigg|_{40}^{65},$$

since $T_x = \int_x^\infty \ell_y \, dy$ so that $\frac{d}{dx} T_x = -\ell_x$, and $Y_x = \int_x^\infty T_y \, dy$ so that $\frac{d}{dx} Y_x = -T_x$. Then the integral evaluates to

$$- 65 T_{65} - Y_{65} + 40 T_{40} + Y_{40} = 40 T_{40} - 65 T_{65} + Y_{40} - Y_{65}. \qquad \square$$

Example 5.8

Find the total past lifetime after age 30 for those now alive aged 40 to 65.

Solution

This is given by

$$\int_{40}^{65} (y-30)\ell_y \, dy = -(y-30)T_y \Big|_{40}^{65} + \int_{40}^{65} T_y \, dy$$

$$= -(y-30)T_y - Y_y \Big|_{40}^{65}$$

$$= 10\, T_{40} - 35\, T_{65} + Y_{40} - Y_{65}. \qquad \Box$$

Example 5.9

Find the average present attained age of those persons now living between ages x and $x+n$ who will ultimately attain age $x+m$.

Solution

The average age is given by the ratio $\dfrac{\text{total past lifetime}}{\text{total population}}$. Thus we have

$$\frac{\int_0^n (x+t)\, \ell_{x+m} \, dt}{\int_0^n \ell_{x+m} \, dt} = \frac{\left(xt + \dfrac{t^2}{2}\right)\ell_{x+m}\Big|_0^n}{t\cdot \ell_{x+m}\Big|_0^n}$$

$$= \frac{\left(nx + \dfrac{n^2}{2}\right)\ell_{x+m}}{n\cdot \ell_{x+m}}$$

$$= x + \frac{n}{2}.$$

A practical use of this result arises if we are asked to determine the average service of an employment group now alive between ages x and $x+n$ who will ultimately attain the age of eligibility for a retirement benefit which is set at age $x+m$. $\qquad \Box$

Example 5.10

Find the average age at death for those persons now alive aged 30 to 55 who will die before age 65.

Solution

The number of members is given by

$$\int_{30}^{55}\int_0^{65-y} \ell_{y+t}\mu_{y+t}\ dt\ dy = \int_{30}^{55} -\ell_{y+t}\Big|_0^{65-y}\ dy$$

$$= \int_{30}^{55} (\ell_y - \ell_{65})\ dy$$

$$= -T_y - y\cdot\ell_{65}\Big|_{30}^{55}$$

$$= T_{30} - T_{55} - 25\ell_{65}. \tag{A}$$

The total life years is given by $\int_{30}^{55}\int_0^{65-y}(y+t)\ell_{y+t}\mu_{y+t}\ dt\ dy$, where y represents past life years and t represents future life years. Evaluating the inside integral we obtain

$$\int_{30}^{55}\Big[-(y+t)\ell_{y+t} - T_{y+t}\Big]_0^{65-y}\ dy = \int_{30}^{55}(y\cdot\ell_y + T_y - 65\ell_{65} - T_{65})\ dy.$$

Note that $\int_{30}^{55} y\cdot\ell_y\ dy = -y\cdot T_y\Big|_{30}^{55} + \int_{30}^{55} T_y\ dy = -y\cdot T_y - Y_y\Big|_{30}^{55}$. Then

$$\int_{30}^{55}(y\cdot\ell_y + T_y - 65\ell_{65} - T_{65})\ dy$$

$$= -y\cdot T_y - 2Y_y - 65y\cdot\ell_{65} - y\cdot T_{65}\Big|_{30}^{55}$$

$$= -55T_{55} - 2Y_{55} - 65(55)\ell_{65} - 55T_{65}$$

$$\qquad + 30T_{30} + 2Y_{30} + 65(30)\ell_{65} + 30T_{65}$$

$$= 30T_{30} + 2Y_{30} - 55T_{55} - 2Y_{55} - 25(65\ell_{65} + T_{65}). \tag{B}$$

Finally the average age at death is given by $\dfrac{(B)}{(A)}$.   □

In general, problems of this type can be solved by using the double integral

$$\int_{y_1}^{y_2}\int_{t_1}^{t_2} f(y,t)\ell_{y+t}\mu_{y+t}\ dt\ dy. \tag{5.8}$$

In Equation (5.8) we would use $f(y,t) = 1$ to find the number of members, $f(y,t) = y$ to find total past lifetime, $f(y,t) = t$ to find total future lifetime, and $f(y,t) = y+t$ to find total lifetime.

Note that all previous examples in this chapter were special cases of this general situation, with fewer restrictions given. For instance, Example 5.7 asked for the total past lifetime for those now aged 40 to 65. There was no restriction on time of death, so the solution is correctly given by

$$\int_{40}^{65}\int_{0}^{\infty} y \cdot \ell_{y+t}\mu_{y+t} \; dt \; dy = \int_{40}^{65}\left(y \cdot -\ell_{y+t}\Big|_{0}^{\infty}\right) dy$$

$$= \int_{40}^{65} y \cdot \ell_{y} \; dy, \quad \text{as before.}$$

Example 5.11

Find the average age at death for those persons now living between ages 30 and 65 who will die between ages 60 and 80.

Solution

Since the two age intervals overlap, the integral expression must be

$$\int_{30}^{60}\int_{60-y}^{80-y} f(y,t)\ell_{y+t}\mu_{y+t} \; dt \; dy + \int_{60}^{65}\int_{0}^{80-y} f(y,t)\ell_{y+t}\mu_{y+t} \; dt \; dy.$$

Using $f(y,t) = 1$ for number of members and $f(y,t) = y+t$ for total lifetime, we find the average age at death to be

$$\frac{1800\ell_{60} + 90T_{60} + 2Y_{60} - 65T_{65} - 2Y_{65} - 2800\ell_{80} - 35T_{80}}{30\ell_{60} + T_{60} - T_{65} - 35\ell_{80}}.$$ □

Example 5.12

Find the total lifetime of those in a stationary population now living between ages 30 and 65 who will die between ages 60 and 80, and within 40 years from now.

Solution

Ignoring the final restriction for the moment, the split integral solution of Example 5.11 applies and we have

$$\int_{30}^{60}\int_{60-y}^{80-y} f(y,t)\ell_{y+t}\mu_{y+t} \; dt \; dy + \int_{60}^{65}\int_{0}^{80-y} f(y,t)\ell_{y+t}\mu_{y+t} \; dt \; dy.$$

The final phrase "*and within* 40 *years from now*" further restricts the first double integral, but not the second, leading to the three double integrals

$$\int_{30}^{40}\int_{60-y}^{40}\cdots+\int_{40}^{60}\int_{60-y}^{80-y}\cdots+\int_{60}^{65}\int_{0}^{80-y}\cdots.$$

Evaluating the integrals we find the total lifetime to be

$$1800\ell_{60}+90T_{60}+2Y_{60}-65T_{65}-2Y_{65}$$

$$-2000\ell_{80}-70T_{70}-2Y_{70}+55T_{80}+2Y_{80}.\qquad\square$$

| Example 5.13 |

Find the average age at death for those alive aged 50 to 60 on January 1, 1980 who will die between ages 65 and 75 in years 1986 through 1990.

| Solution |

Death must take place between January 1, 1986 and January 1, 1991, which is between 6 years from now and 11 years from now. Ignoring this time constraint for the moment, the double integral would be

$$\int_{50}^{60}\int_{65-y}^{75-y}f(y,t)\ell_{y+t}\mu_{y+t}\,dt\,dy.$$

Taking into account the time constraints, the integrals become

$$\int_{54}^{59}\int_{65-y}^{11}\cdots+\int_{59}^{60}\int_{6}^{11}\cdots.$$

Note that it is impossible for anyone now alive between ages 50 and 54 to comply with all the conditions. Evaluating the integrals we find the average age at death to be

$$\frac{5(65\ell_{65}+T_{65})-(66T_{66}+2Y_{66})+(71T_{71}+2Y_{71})}{5\ell_{65}-T_{66}+T_{71}}.\qquad\square$$

5.4 THE LEXIS DIAGRAM

Over the years many ingenious methods have been devised to facilitate the solution of stationary population problems. In one of the earlier papers, Veit [29] applied the concept of the *Lexis diagram*, shown in Figure 5.3, to these problems. (In Figures 5.1 and 5.2, earlier in this chapter, we used Lexis diagrams to help define the stationary population. In this section we use them to assist us in doing population analysis.)

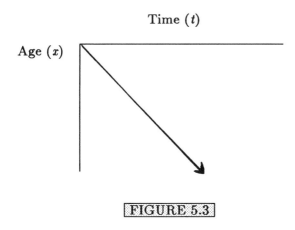

Time (*t*)

Age (*x*)

FIGURE 5.3

The following are the features of the Lexis diagram.

(1) A fixed point in time is represented by a vertical line.
(2) A fixed age is represented by a horizontal line.
(3) All individuals move along a 45° path, downward and to the right, since with each passing unit of time they increase in age by that same unit.

The use of the Lexis diagram permits very short solutions to some problems previously considered. To illustrate this point we will revisit Examples 5.11, 5.12, and 5.13.

Example 5.11R

Find the average age at death for those persons now living between ages 30 and 65 who will die between ages 60 and 80.

Solution

The group is defined as all those now aged 30 to 65 aging along their respective 45° paths as shown in Figure 5.4, but restricted to only those who die between ages 60 and 80 as shown by the horizontal lines. Hence we wish to analyze the members of the group who die in the shaded area.

We can think of the shaded area as a country, with borders of two types: land (horizontal and vertical borders) and water (diagonal borders). Migration in and out of the country is allowed only by land. Furthermore, migration into the country can take place only along the northern and western borders, and migration out of the country only along eastern and southern borders. The "in and out" method allows us to easily determine the number of members in the group being analyzed.

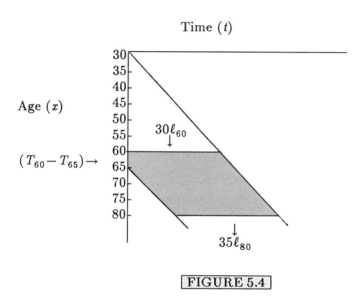

FIGURE 5.4

INS: Anyone entering the country along the northern border is exactly age 60, so the number of immigrants here is represented by the symbol ℓ_{60}. Furthermore, because the border is 30 units long, the total number of immigrants from the north will be $30\ell_{60}$. The people entering along the western border are those alive aged 60 to 65, and are represented by $(T_{60} - T_{65})$.

OUTS: The number of emigrants to the south is $35\ell_{80}$, using similar reasoning as for the northern immigrants. There are no emigrants to the east.

The population to be analyzed is therefore $30\ell_{60} + T_{60} - T_{65} - 35\ell_{80}$. Note how much more quickly we reached that result here compared to the integral approach in Example 5.11.

Grace and Nesbitt [11] show that the total lifetime for any ℓ_x group of persons is $x \cdot \ell_x + T_x$, and the total lifetime for any T_x group is $x \cdot T_x + 2Y_x$. Using the Grace-Nesbitt method the total lifetime of our group is easily found to be

$$30(60\ell_{60} + T_{60}) + 60T_{60} + 2Y_{60} - 65T_{65} - 2Y_{65} - 35(80\ell_{80} + T_{80})$$

$$= 1800\ell_{60} + 90T_{60} + 2Y_{60} - 65T_{65} - 2Y_{65} - 2800\ell_{80} - 35T_{80}.$$

The average age at death follows by dividing this value by the number of deaths. □

Example 5.12R

Find the total lifetime of those in a stationary population now living between ages 30 and 65 who will die between ages 60 and 80, and within 40 years from now.

Solution

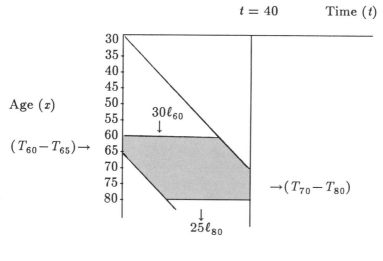

FIGURE 5.5

In this example we have the additional limit that all deaths must take place within the next 40 years. Since this is a constant time limit it can be represented by the vertical line at $t=40$ as shown. From Figure 5.5 we can easily determine the number of members in the shaded area.

INS: $30\ell_{60}$ (from the north) plus $T_{60} - T_{65}$ (from the west).
OUTS: $25\ell_{80}$ (to the south) plus $T_{70} - T_{80}$ (to the east).

The number of members is

$$30\ell_{60} + (T_{60} - T_{65}) - 25\ell_{80} - (T_{70} - T_{80}),$$

and using the Grace-Nesbitt technique the total lifetime is

$$30(60\ell_{60} + T_{60}) + 60T_{60} + 2Y_{60}$$

$$- 65T_{65} - 2Y_{65} - 25(80\ell_{80} + T_{80}) - 70T_{70} - 2Y_{70} + 80T_{80} + 2Y_{80}.$$

$$\square$$

Example 5.13R

Find the average age at death for those alive aged 50 to 60 on January 1, 1980 who will die between ages 65 and 75 in years 1986 through 1990.

Solution

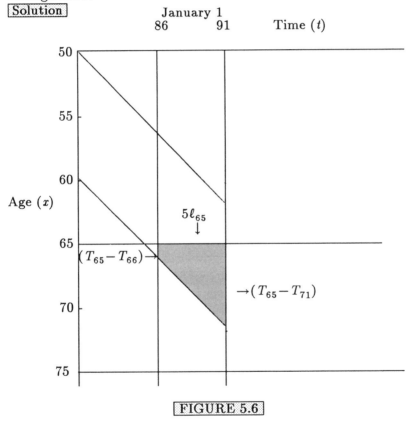

FIGURE 5.6

INS: $5\ell_{65}$ (from the north) plus $T_{65} - T_{66}$ (from the west).

OUTS: $T_{65} - T_{71}$ (to the east).

The number of deaths is

$$5\ell_{65} + (T_{65} - T_{66}) - (T_{65} - T_{71}) = 5\ell_{65} + T_{71} - T_{66},$$

with total lifetime

$$5(65\ell_{65} + T_{65}) + 71T_{71} + 2Y_{71} - 66T_{66} - 2Y_{66}.$$

The average age at death is found by the usual division.　　　□

| Example 5.14 |

Find an expression for the average *attained* age of those persons in the stationary population now between ages 30 and 40 who will die prior to age 50.

| Solution |

We use the Lexis diagram to determine the number of deaths, which is $T_{30} - T_{40} - 10\ell_{50}$.

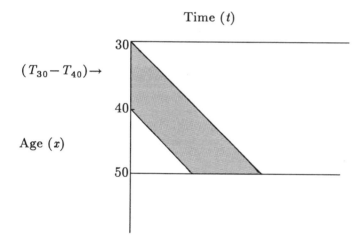

Time (t)

$(T_{30} - T_{40}) \rightarrow$

Age (x)

| FIGURE 5.7 |

The average attained age now of those deaths would be the total of their current attained ages divided by the number of them.

　　The Grace-Nesbitt technique, which easily gives the total of ages at death for a defined group of deaths, does not apply to the problem of finding total attained ages. We will use the following reasoning approach for this problem, and then verify the result by integration.

We first note that total of attained ages is the same as total past lifetime. Thus we seek the total past lifetime (TPL) as of now for those who will go on to die before age 50. Note that the number of deaths are the INS $(T_{30} - T_{40})$ minus the OUTS $(10\ell_{50})$, so the TPL of the deaths can be found as the TPL of the INS minus the TPL of the OUTS.

The $T_{30} - T_{40}$ INS have TPL up to age 30 of $30(T_{30} - T_{40})$, and they have TPL since age 30 of $(Y_{30} - Y_{40} - 10T_{40})$, for a total TPL of $30T_{30} - 40T_{40} + Y_{30} - Y_{40}$. Note that this result is verified by Example 5.7.

The $10\ell_{50}$ OUTS are evenly distributed over the 10-year-long age 50 line, so they were evenly distributed on the vertical at the now point of time. This means their average attained age now is 35, so the TPL now of the eventual survivors to age 50 is $35 \cdot 10\ell_{50} = 350\ell_{50}$. Note that this result is verified by Example 5.9.

Then the TPL now of the deaths is

$$30T_{30} - 40T_{40} + Y_{30} - Y_{40} - 350\ell_{50},$$

so their average attained age now is

$$\frac{30T_{30} - 40T_{40} + Y_{30} - Y_{40} - 350\ell_{50}}{T_{30} - T_{40} - 10\ell_{50}}$$

$$= 30 + \frac{Y_{30} - Y_{40} - 10T_{40} - 50\ell_{50}}{T_{30} - T_{40} - 10\ell_{50}}.$$

To verify our reasoning by the integral approach, we can use the general double integral of (5.8) to find the total of attained ages now of the defined deaths as

$$\int_{30}^{40} \int_0^{50-y} y \cdot \ell_{y+t}\mu_{y+t}\, dt\, dy.$$

Integrating by parts we obtain

$$\int_{30}^{40} (y \cdot \ell_y - y \cdot \ell_{50})\, dy,$$

which in turn evaluates to $30T_{30} - 40T_{40} + Y_{30} - Y_{40} - 350\ell_{50}$, as expected.   □

For a further analysis of the problem of finding average attained ages, see Brown and Lutek [6].

5.5 FURTHER APPLICATIONS

If a population can be modeled as stationary, then there is a large number of practical applications. A small sample of such applications follows.

| Example 5.15 |

In a stationary community supported by 5000 annual births, each person contributes 2000 on attaining age 25 and 100 on each succeeding birthday up to, and including, the 65th birthday. On each birthday thereafter an annuity payment of 1500 is made. A payment of 500 is made at the death of each contributor who dies before receiving the first annuity payment. Find expressions for (a) the constant number of persons who have made their first contribution but not their last, (b) the receipts in any year, (c) the total annuity payments in any year, and (d) the death claims in any year.

| Solution |

(a) This is given by the number alive between ages 25 and 65, which is $\dfrac{5000}{\ell_0} (T_{25} - T_{65})$.

(b) Receipts: $\dfrac{5000}{\ell_0} \left[2000\ell_{25} + 100(\ell_{26} + \ell_{27} + \cdots + \ell_{65}) \right]$

$$= \frac{5000\ell_{25}}{\ell_0} \left(2000 + 100 \cdot e_{25:\overline{40}|} \right)$$

(c) Annuity Payments: $\dfrac{5000}{\ell_0} \cdot 1500(\ell_{66} + \ell_{67} + \cdots)$

$$= \frac{5000}{\ell_0} \cdot 1500 \ell_{65}\, e_{65}$$

(d) Death Claims: $\dfrac{5000}{\ell_0}(d_{25} + d_{26} + \cdots + d_{65})(500)$

$$= \frac{5000}{\ell_0}(\ell_{25} - \ell_{66})(500) \qquad\qquad \square$$

Example 5.16

A country maintains a stationary militia of 100,000 men by continuously drafting recruits at age 21 for a period of 5 years of service. Recruits are paid 20 per day for the first 2 years and 30 per day for the final 3 years. In the event of death in service, a death benefit is payable equal to the total of a recruit's pay to date of death. The survivors are discharged on completion of their term of service with a bonus of 2000. Express each of the following in terms of the population symbols ℓ, L, T, or Y.

(a) The number of new entrants each year
(b) The annual pay bill for the militia
(c) The average death benefit payable, assuming a uniform distribution of deaths in any year
(d) The total discharge bonuses payable each year

Solution

(a) Let the number of new entrants be x.

Then $100,000 = \frac{x}{\ell_{21}}(T_{21} - T_{26})$, so that $x = \frac{100,000\ell_{21}}{T_{21} - T_{26}}$.

(b) The annual pay bill is

$$\frac{x}{\ell_{21}}\Big[20(365)(L_{21} + L_{22}) + 30(365)(L_{23} + L_{24} + L_{25})\Big]$$

$$= \frac{x}{\ell_{21}}\Big[20(365)(T_{21} + .5T_{23} - 1.5T_{26})\Big].$$

(c) Assuming UDD and remembering that pay starts at 20 per day but rises to 30 per day, the average death benefit is given by

$$365\left(\frac{10d_{21} + 30d_{22} + 55d_{23} + 85d_{24} + 115d_{25}}{\ell_{21} - \ell_{26}}\right).$$

(d) The total amount of discharge bonuses is $\frac{x}{\ell_{21}} \cdot 2000\ell_{26}$.   □

Example 5.17

A company has a pension plan for its workers. Workers are hired at age 20 and immediately start earning pension credits. However, they do not gain legal rights to their pension credits until age 30. Retirement is at age 65. The only other cause of decrement is death. The workers form a stationary population. Find the number of years of pensionable service for which the plan sponsor is now responsible (*i.e.*, the years of pensionable service since age 20 of the members of a stationary population now alive between ages 30 and 65).

Solution
Number of members: $\int_{30}^{65} \ell_y \, dy = -T_y\big|_{30}^{65} = T_{30} - T_{65}.$
Past service since age 20:

$$\int_{30}^{65} \frac{(y-20)}{dy} \begin{vmatrix} \ell_y \, dy \\ -T_y \end{vmatrix} = -(y-20)T_y\bigg|_{30}^{65} + \int_{30}^{65} T_y \, dy$$

$$= -(y-20)T_y - Y_y\bigg|_{30}^{65}$$

$$= 10\,T_{30} + Y_{30} - 45\,T_{65} - Y_{65}. \qquad \square$$

Example 5.18

In a country with a stationary population of k, consideration is being given to an old-age benefit program under which a uniform yearly payment would be made to each person aged 65 and over. The benefit would be paid from a tax of c percent of earned incomes of working members aged 20 through 64. It has been estimated that the percentages who are gainfully employed and the average yearly earnings of those so employed are as given in the following table.

TABLE 5.1

Age	Percent Gainfully Employed	Average Yearly Earnings of Gainfully Employed
20-24	70	20,000
25-54	90	30,000
55-64	80	40,000

Find expressions for (a) the total annual tax yield and (b) the uniform yearly benefit which would be provided under the program.

Solution
(a) The annual tax yield (ATY) is given by

$$(.01c)\left(\frac{k}{T_0}\right)[(.70)(20{,}000)(T_{20}-T_{25}) + (.90)(30{,}000)(T_{25}-T_{55})$$

$$+ (.80)(40{,}000)(T_{55}-T_{65})]$$

$$= \left(\frac{ck}{T_0}\right)(140\,T_{20} + 130\,T_{25} + 50\,T_{55} - 320\,T_{65}).$$

(b) The uniform yearly benefit is $\frac{T_0}{k}\cdot\frac{ATY}{T_{65}}$, since it is simply the ATY distributed to the population over age 65. $\qquad \square$

| Example 5.19 |

The number of residents in a certain home for the aged is maintained in a stationary condition by admitting 100 new residents each year uniformly throughout the year. The ages at entry are given in the following table.

| TABLE 5.2 |

Exact Age at Entry	Number of Entrants
66	25
67	35
68	25
69	10
70	5

From entry, residents are given a personal allowance of 100 per week until they have been in the institution for two years or have attained age 70, whichever happens *later*, after which the allowance is increased to 200 per week. Give expressions for (a) the number of increases of personal allowances granted each year, and (b) the total amount of personal allowances paid each year, assuming the mortality of these lives follows a standard mortality table.

| Solution |

(a)   Number of increases is given by

$$25\frac{\ell_{70}}{\ell_{66}} + 35\frac{\ell_{70}}{\ell_{67}} + 25\frac{\ell_{70}}{\ell_{68}} + 10\frac{\ell_{71}}{\ell_{69}} + 5\frac{\ell_{72}}{\ell_{70}}.$$

(b)   The total amount of annual personal allowances is given by

$$5200\left[25\frac{T_{66} + T_{70}}{\ell_{66}} + 35\frac{T_{67} + T_{70}}{\ell_{67}} + 25\frac{T_{68} + T_{70}}{\ell_{68}} \right.$$
$$\left. + 10\frac{T_{69} + T_{71}}{\ell_{69}} + 5\frac{T_{70} + T_{72}}{\ell_{70}} \right].$$

□

5.6 EXERCISES

5.1 Introduction; 5.2 Analysis of the Survivorship Group

5-1. Find the average age at death for those in the survivorship group who survive to age 40 but die before age 65.

5.3 The Stationary Population; 5.4 The Lexis Diagram

5-2. There are two stationary populations. The force of mortality is .015 at all ages in the first population, and for the second population $S(x) = 1 - \frac{x}{100}$. Calculate the difference in the average age at death for all deaths in any year in the two populations (in absolute value).

5-3. In a certain stationary population, $\ell_x = a - x$ for $0 \le x \le a$, and $\overset{\circ}{e}_0 = 60$. Find the average age of the total population.

5-4. A maternity hospital delivers 100 babies per week. 70% of them leave the hospital by the end of one week, 20% of those remaining leave by the end of two weeks, 50% of those remaining leave by the end of three weeks, and the rest leave by the end of four weeks.

    (a) Assuming a uniform distribution of decrements, how many babies are in the maternity ward at any time?
    (b) What is the average length of stay for a baby?

5-5. An hourly-rated staff is maintained in a stationary condition by 3000 annual entrants at exact age 25. 20% leave after 10 years, 10% of those remaining are promoted after 20 years into jobs outside the hourly-rated staff, and the balance retire on a pension at age 65. Find each of the following.

    (a) The size of the staff.
    (b) The number promoted each year.
    (c) The number of pensioners on the books.

5-6. Show that in a stationary population, the crude birth rate and the crude death rate (defined in Chapter 2) are the inverse of the life expectancy at birth.

5-7. A company with 1000 employees is kept in a stationary state by admission of a uniform number of entrants at exact age 25. There are no decrements other than death, except that $\frac{1}{4}$ of those who reach age 60 retire and $\frac{1}{3}$ of those who reach age 62 retire. The remainder all retire at age 65. Find (a) the number of annual entrants at age 25, and (b) the total number of deaths in service each year.

5-8. The University of Waterloo wants to have 4000 undergraduate math majors in a stationary condition. 80% of admission offers result in enrollment. 25% of the students leave (or die) in Year 1, 20% of those remaining leave (or die) in Year 2, 10% of those remaining leave (or die) in Year 3, and 5% of those remaining leave (or die) in Year 4 prior to graduation. The rest graduate. Determine the number of freshmen admission offers that should be made, assuming a uniform distribution of decrements.

5-9. A pet store maintains a stationary population of 450 goldfish. You are given that (i) a newly acquired goldfish has an expectation of remaining in the store 3.0 days, and (ii) each day twice as many goldfish die as are sold. Determine how many goldfish are sold each day.

5-10. In a stationary population of 60,000 lives, $\frac{1}{3}$ of the population is under age 21. Given that $\overset{o}{e}_{21} = 50$, find ℓ_{21}.

5-11. In a life table $\overset{o}{e}_0 = 69.89$ $\overset{o}{e}_{75} = 8.70$

$\ell_0 = 100,000$ $\ell_{75} = 48,170$

What proportion of the corresponding stationary population is 75 years or older?

5-12. In a life table whose radix is 100,000, we find the following values.

$$\overset{\circ}{e}_0 = 68.23$$
$$\overset{\circ}{e}_{75} = 8.52$$

If 6% of the corresponding stationary population is 75 or older, find $S(75)$.

5-13. A large industrial union is planning a retirement community for its members. The union has reached a stationary condition, with 480 members reaching age 65 and retiring each year. Assume that retirements are distributed uniformly throughout the year, and that the number of retired living members attaining age x in any year is $\ell_x = \frac{3}{10}(105-x)^2$, for $0 < x < 105$. Find the total number of retired members.

5-14. An army is kept in a stationary condition with 1000 conscripts per year at age 20. All survivors retire at age 50. If $\mu_x = .015$, $20 < x < 50$, how many person-years of service are provided by the 1000 20-year-olds who enter in any year?

5-15. Given a stationary population, determine the average attained age of those now alive between ages 20 and 65.

5-16. Find an expression for the number of people now alive aged 20 to 40 who will die between ages 30 and 65.

5-17. In a stationary population, for those now living between ages 20 and 30, find the number who will die between ages 65 and 75 and within the next 50 years.

5-18. Among people who attain exact age 65 between time 10 and time 20, determine the number who die before exact age 75 and before time 25.

5-19. For a stationary population supported by ℓ_0 births, find each of the following.

    (a) The total number of deaths among those now aged 25 to 27 in the next 5 years.

    (b) The average age at death of those dying between 65 and 70 from among those now alive aged 20 to 30.

    (c) The number of years lived in the next two years by all those now aged 25 and over who die before attaining age 30.

5-20. Prove that for the $T_\alpha - T_\beta$ persons now living between ages α and β, the quantity $\left[Y_\alpha - Y_\beta - (\beta - \alpha) T_\beta\right]$ represents both their past lifetime since age α as well as their future lifetime before age β.

5.5 Further Applications

5-21. A particular manufacturing company hires 2000 new employees each year at exact age 21. 20% of the employees retire at exact age 55 and receive a pension of 20,000 per annum for life. The rest of the employees retire at exact age 65 and receive an annual pension of 30,000 for life. There are no decrements except death and retirement. Determine expressions for (a) the number of active employees in the company, (b) the number of pensioners at any time, and (c) the annual cost of the pension benefits.

5-22. In a small country with a stationary population, a special system is used for supporting the aged. On January 1, each person whose age last birthday is between 20 and 64, inclusive, contributes 100 to a pool. On the same date, payments of k dollars are made from the pool to all persons 65 and over, with the entire pool split up among all eligible recipients.

    (a) Find k.

    (b) Assume (i) $k = 500$, (ii) twice as many persons attain age 20 as attain age 65 in a calendar year, and (iii) the complete expectation of life at age 65 is 15 years. What is the complete expectation of life at age 20?

CHAPTER 6

STABLE POPULATION THEORY

6.1 INTRODUCTION

The conditions required to create the stationary population model of Chapter 5 are seldom realized in practice, so the opportunities to apply the mathematical results derived in Chapter 5 are very limited. Recall that the stationary population model is based on two assumptions, namely (a) that the annual number of births is constant and evenly distributed over the year, and (b) the applicable mortality profile, normally viewed in terms of the traditional life table, remains constant over time.

In this chapter we introduce a population model, called a *stable population*, that differs from the stationary model by allowing for variation in the population's birth rate. The second requirement of the stationary model, that of constant mortality over time, remains an assumption of the new model of this chapter as well.

The birth pattern in the type of population analyzed in this chapter is governed by an assumed fertility profile, or fertility model. This model is assumed to hold constant over time. Because fertility rates tend to be estimated from data in sex-distinct form, it follows that population analysis is sex-distinct as well. As pointed out in Chapter 2, male fertility rates are difficult to estimate. Thus our population analysis in this chapter will be presumed to deal with female populations only. (Techniques for analyzing male populations make use of sex-ratios of male to female births; these techniques are not pursued further in this text.)

A fertility profile is defined by specifying a set of discrete age-and-sex-specific rates of the form f_x^f, or $_nf_x^f$, as defined in

Chapter 2, just as a mortality profile is defined by specifying a set of discrete age-and-sex-specific mortality rates of the form q_x^f.

Both mortality and fertility profiles can be defined by continuous functions, as an alternative to the discrete functions described in the previous paragraph. In this case a mortality profile is completely defined by specifying a *survival distribution function*, denoted by $S(x)$, which is a continuous function giving the probability that a newborn life will survive to age x. Thus $S(x)$ is equivalent to the life table symbol $_xp_0$. Alternatively, a mortality profile can be defined by specifying a *force of mortality*, denoted by μ_x, and related to the survival function by the relationship

$$S(x) \;=\; _xp_0 \;=\; e^{-\int_0^x \mu_y \, dy}, \tag{6.1}$$

which follows directly from Equation (3.17).

In a continuous model, the fertility profile would be defined by a continuous sex-distinct *fertility function*, which we will denote by ϕ_x^f for our female models. (Note that we will use the terms mortality and fertility *rates* for discrete models, and mortality (or survival) and fertility *functions* for continuous models.) This function is the continuous annual rate at which women exactly age x are giving birth to female offspring.

6.2 THE FOUNDATIONS OF STABLE POPULATION THEORY

In this section we will describe several properties of the stable population model, assuming that the fixed mortality and fertility profiles are defined by a continuous survival function and a continuous fertility function, respectively. Recall that we are presuming a female population throughout this discussion.

Let $B(t)$ denote the annual rate at which female births are occurring in a population at time t, so that $B(t) \, dt$ is the differential number of female births during the time interval from t to $t+dt$. Then the number of births in one year is given by

$$B \;=\; \int_0^1 B(t) \, dt. \tag{6.2}$$

If $B(t)$ were constant over time, then the number of births would be B in any annual period. This is the case in a stationary population, with $B=\ell_0$.

For the more general stable population, however, $B(t)$ is presumed to vary with t in the manner defined by the relationship

$$B(t+n) = B(t) \cdot e^{n \cdot r_i}. \tag{6.3}$$

This relationship shows that the annual rate of births grows over time at a continuous instantaneous rate of r_i. If $r_i > 0$, then the rate of births is increasing over time, and if $r_i < 0$ the rate of births is decreasing. If $r_i = 0$, the rate of births is constant over time. Thus we see that a stationary population is a special case of a stable population with $r_i = 0$.

The continuous instantaneous growth rate r_i is analogous to the continuous instantaneous growth rate for a fund of money due to interest, and such rate is called the force of interest. Accordingly we can refer to r_i as the *force of growth* for the annual rate of births in the population.

Although we initially define r_i as the force of growth in the rate of births, because mortality is constant over time it follows that r_i is the force of growth of the population itself. This very important result is derived in the following example.

Example 6.1

Show that if the annual rate of births in a population varies according to Equation (6.3), and if mortality is constant over time, then the size of the population will likewise vary according to the relationship

$$P(t+n) = P(t) \cdot e^{n \cdot r_i}. \tag{6.4}$$

Solution

Let the population be of size $P(t)$ at time t, with rate of births $B(t)$. Then, by Equation (6.3) the rate of births at time $t-x$ is

$$B(t-x) = B(t) \cdot e^{-r_i x},$$

and the rate of persons surviving from birth at time $t-x$ to age x at time t is $B(t-x) \cdot S(x)$. The differential number of persons alive at time t at age x (or, more properly, between ages x and $x+dx$) is

$$F_x(t)\, dx = B(t-x) \cdot S(x)\, dx, \tag{6.5}$$

so the total female population at time t is

$$P(t) = \int_0^\infty F_x(t)\,dx = \int_0^\infty B(t-x) \cdot S(x)\,dx$$

$$= \int_0^\infty B(t) \cdot e^{-r_i x} \cdot S(x)\,dx. \qquad (6.6a)$$

Similarly, the total female population at time $t+n$ is

$$P(t+n) = \int_0^\infty F_x(t+n)\,dx = \int_0^\infty B(t+n) \cdot e^{-r_i x} \cdot S(x)\,dx. \qquad (6.6b)$$

Note that the $S(x)$ terms in (6.6a) and (6.6b) are the same, since mortality is constant over time, and $B(t+n) = B(t) \cdot e^{n \cdot r_i}$ from Equation (6.3). Thus we have

$$P(t+n) = e^{n \cdot r_i} \int_0^\infty B(t) \cdot e^{-r_i x} \cdot S(x)\,dx$$

$$= e^{n \cdot r_i} \cdot P(t). \qquad \Box$$

The result of Example 6.1 is very important. It shows that the force of growth in the rate of births is the force of growth of the population itself. The rate r_i is called the *intrinsic rate of growth* of the population. One of the properties of a stable population is that it has a constant intrinsic rate of growth, in the form of a continuous instantaneous rate, also called a force of growth. A second basic property of a stable population is developed in the following example.

| Example 6.2 |

Determine the proportion of a stable population that is between ages x and $x+dx$ at time t.

| Solution |

From Example 6.1 we know that the number of people between ages x and $x+dx$ at time t is $F_x(t)\,dx$, given by (6.5), and the total population at time t is $P(t)$, given by (6.6). Then the desired proportion is

$$\frac{F_x(t)\,dx}{P(t)} = \frac{B(t) \cdot e^{-r_i x} \cdot S(x)\,dx}{\int_0^\infty B(t) \cdot e^{-r_i x} \cdot S(x)\,dx}.$$

Since $B(t)$ is not a function of x, this proportion reduces to

$$\frac{F_x(t)\,dx}{P(t)} = \frac{e^{-r_i x} \cdot S(x)\,dx}{\int_0^\infty e^{-r_i x} \cdot S(x)\,dx}.$$

□

The important implication of Example 6.2 is that the *proportion* of the population in any age interval is not a function of t, and is thus the same proportion at *any* point in time. Of course the *number* of people in an age interval changes over time (at force of growth r_i), but the proportion of the population in that interval does not change.

Thus we have reached a definition of the stable population, as one in which the proportion of the population in any age group remains the same over time, and the population, as well as its different age groups, grows (or declines) at a constant intrinsic rate of increase (or decrease). Further, the stable population will be subject to fixed mortality and fertility profiles over time.

In a work published in 1911, Sharpe and Lotka (see Keyfitz and Smith [18], pp. 93-108) proved that a closed population experiencing fixed fertility and mortality profiles will, regardless of its *initial age distribution*, eventually develop an asymptotically stable age distribution and eventually increase (or decrease) at a constant rate. We will explore this statement more fully in Chapter 7 by actually illustrating the achievement of asymptotic stability given constant fertility and mortality profiles. Because stability is only an asymptotic property, convergence to stability can be very slow. As will be illustrated in Chapter 7, we can select an arbitrary population with any age distribution but with fixed fertility and mortality profiles. If that population is then projected, it will converge to a stable distribution of age groups. It will never achieve full stability, however, as can be seen if enough decimal places are carried in the calculations.

Figure 6.1 illustrates the Sharpe-Lotka theorem. Starting with two very different populations, East Germany in 1957 and Thailand in 1955, Bourgeois-Pichat [3] show that projections using constant mortality and fertility assumptions ultimately lead to populations that have the same proportion of the population in different age groups, and the same intrinsic rate of increase.

The diagrams in Figure 6.1 are called **population pyramids**. They are normally presented as sideways histograms showing the proportion of the population in various age groups, usually quinquennial. The male population proportions are shown on the left, and the female proportions on the right. We will examine population pyramids further in Example 6.7.

An outline of the proof of the Sharpe-Lotka theorem is given in Appendix D, along with other interesting properties of the stable population that are otherwise beyond the scope of this text.

Projected Populations Illustrating the Sharpe-Lotka Theorem

East Germany

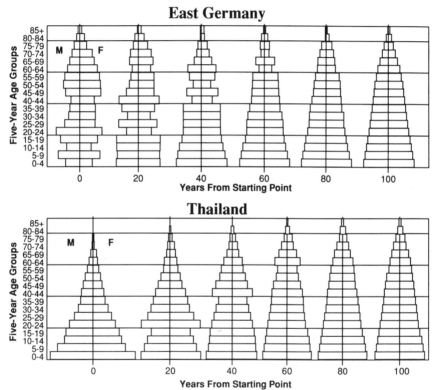

Thailand

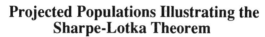

FIGURE 6.1

Next we derive a very important relationship called the *characteristic equation* of the stable population. Recall from Example 6.1 that the differential number of people (women, since we are assuming a female population) alive at age x at time t is

$$F_x(t)\, dx \;=\; B(t) \cdot e^{-r_i x} \cdot S(x)\, dx.$$

These women are subject to the female fertility function given by ϕ_x^f, so the differential rate of births at time t is given by $B(t) \cdot e^{-r_i x} \cdot S(x) \cdot \phi_x^f\, dx$. When this is integrated over all x, the rate of births in the population at time t results. Thus we have

$$B(t) \;=\; \int_0^\infty B(t) \cdot e^{-r_i x} \cdot S(x) \cdot \phi_x^f\, dx, \tag{6.7}$$

which, upon division by $B(t)$, yields the characteristic equation

$$\int_0^\infty e^{-r_i x} \cdot S(x) \cdot \phi_x^f\, dx \;=\; 1. \tag{6.8}$$

If α and β are the lower and upper limits to the age range of fertility, so that $\phi_x^f = 0$ for $x < \alpha$ and $x > \beta$, then Equation (6.8) can be written as

$$\int_\alpha^\beta e^{-r_i x} \cdot S(x) \cdot \phi_x^f\, dx \;=\; 1. \tag{6.9}$$

This equation states the relationship among the assumed fixed mortality profile (given by $S(x)$), the assumed fixed fertility profile (given by ϕ_x^f), and the intrinsic rate of increase, or force of growth, given by r_i. In particular, if $S(x)$ and ϕ_x^f are given, Equation (6.9) can be solved, at least approximately, for r_i. (In Appendix D it is shown that the characteristic equation has exactly one real root.)

Next we consider the ratio $\dfrac{B(t)}{P(t)}$, which expresses the rate of births at time t per person in the population at that time. This ratio is denoted by b_i. It is constant over time and is an intrinsic characteristic of the stable population; for this reason we call it the *intrinsic birth rate* of the population. Note the distinction between the *annual* rate of births in the population at time t, given by $B(t)$, and the *intrinsic* birth rate for the population, given by b_i.

| Example 6.3 |

Show that the intrinsic birth rate b_i is constant over time and is given by

$$b_i \;=\; \frac{1}{\int_0^\infty e^{-r_i x} \cdot S(x)\, dx}. \tag{6.10}$$

Solution

Taking the expression for $P(t)$ given by Equation (6.6a), we have

$$b_i = \frac{B(t)}{P(t)} = \frac{B(t)}{\int_0^\infty B(t) \cdot e^{-r_i x} \cdot S(x)\, dx} = \frac{1}{\int_0^\infty e^{-r_i x} \cdot S(x)\, dx},$$

as required. Since this expression for b_i does not involve t, it is constant over time. □

Example 6.4

Similarly, define the *intrinsic death rate* of the population to be $d_i = \dfrac{D(t)}{P(t)}$, where $D(t)$ is the annual rate at which deaths are occurring in the population at time t. (Note the similarity between $D(t)$ and $B(t)$.) Show that d_i is constant over time and is given by

$$d_i = b_i \int_0^\infty e^{-r_i x} \cdot S(x) \cdot \mu_x\, dx. \tag{6.11}$$

Solution

We know that $B(t) \cdot e^{-r_i x} \cdot S(x)\, dx$ is the differential number of people at age x at time t, so $B(t) \cdot e^{-r_i x} \cdot S(x) \cdot \mu_x\, dx$ is the differential rate at which deaths are occurring at age x at time t. Then

$$D(t) = \int_0^\infty B(t) \cdot e^{-r_i x} \cdot S(x) \cdot \mu_x\, dx$$

is the annual rate of deaths at time t, and the intrinsic death rate for the population, which is the annual death rate at time t per person in the population, is

$$d_i = \frac{D(t)}{P(t)} = \frac{\int_0^\infty B(t) \cdot e^{-r_i x} \cdot S(x) \cdot \mu_x\, dx}{\int_0^\infty B(t) \cdot e^{-r_i x} \cdot S(x)\, dx}$$

$$= b_i \int_0^\infty e^{-r_i x} \cdot S(x) \cdot \mu_x\, dx,$$

as required, since the $B(t)$ terms cancel and $b_i = \dfrac{1}{\int_0^\infty e^{-r_i x} \cdot S(x)\, dx}$ from Equation (6.10). Since (6.11) does not involve t, we see that d_i is constant over time. □

Example 6.5

Show that if the continuous mortality profile is given by a constant force of mortality, so that $\mu_x = \mu$ for all x, then the intrinsic death rate of the population is equal to that same constant.

Solution

If $\mu_x = \mu$, then, using Equation (6.1), we find that $S(x) = e^{-\mu x}$. Then from Example 6.4 we have

$$d_i = \frac{D(t)}{P(t)} = \frac{\int_0^\infty B(t) \cdot e^{-r_i x} \cdot e^{-\mu x} \cdot \mu \, dx}{\int_0^\infty B(t) \cdot e^{-r_i x} \cdot e^{-\mu x} \, dx} = \mu. \qquad \square$$

Example 6.6

Show that the three intrinsic rates for a stable population are related by

$$d_i = b_i - r_i. \tag{6.12}$$

Solution

From Equation (6.11),

$$d_i = \int_0^\infty b_i \cdot e^{-r_i x} \cdot S(x) \cdot \mu_x \, dx = -\int_0^\infty b_i \cdot e^{-r_i x} \, dS(x),$$

since $\frac{d}{dx} S(x) = -S(x) \cdot \mu_x$. Using integration by parts we have

$$d_i = -b_i \cdot e^{-r_i x} \cdot S(x)\big|_0^\infty - r_i \int_0^\infty b_i \cdot e^{-r_i x} \cdot S(x) \, dx.$$

But $-b_i \cdot e^{-r_i x} \cdot S(x)\big|_0^\infty = b_i$ and $\int_0^\infty b_i \cdot e^{-r_i x} \cdot S(x) \, dx = 1$, from Equation (6.10), so we have $d_i = b_i - r_i$. This equation can then be rewritten to provide a definition of any one of the intrinsic rates in terms of the other two. In particular, $r_i = b_i - d_i$, which is analogous to $r_c = b_c - d_c$ for the crude rates defined in Chapter 2. $\square$

For both a stationary and a stable population the probability of surviving from birth to age x is given by $S(x) = {}_x p_0 = \frac{\ell_x}{\ell_0}$, in terms of functions taken from the life table representing the mortality profile for the population. Let B^z denote the births in calendar year z and $E_x(z)$ denote the number attaining age x in calendar year z in an actual population. Those attaining age x in year z are the survivors of the births in year $z - x$, so we know that $E_x(z) = B^{z-x} \cdot S(x)$, and thus

$$S(x) = \frac{E_x(z)}{B^{z-x}}, \tag{6.13}$$

for both a stationary and a stable population. For a stationary population, $B^{z-x} = B^z$, so the survival function can be expressed in terms of population values as

$$S(x) = \frac{E_x(z)}{B^z}. \tag{6.14a}$$

For a stable population, however, we have the more general relationship $B^{z-x} = B^z \cdot e^{-r_i x}$. Substituting into Equation (6.13) we have

$$S(x) = \frac{E_x(z)}{B^z \cdot e^{-r_i x}} = \frac{E_x(z)}{B^z} \cdot e^{r_i x} \tag{6.14b}$$

as an expression for the survival function in terms of stable population values. Again this illustrates that the stationary population model is the special case of the stable population model with $r_i = 0$.

In the limiting case, as the width of the age groups in a population pyramid approaches zero, the discrete histogram approaches a continuous population function showing the proportion of the population that is between exact ages x and $x+dx$. This continuous version of the histogram is denoted by φ_x, and is illustrated in Figure 6.2.

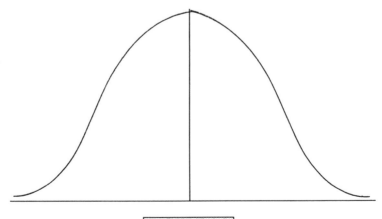

FIGURE 6.2

| Example 6.7 |

By determining the slope of the continuous version of the population pyramid for a stable population, show that a constant change in the force of growth r_i has the same effect on the shape of the pyramid as does the same constant change in the force of mortality μ_x.

Solution

If the population rate of births at time t is $B(t)$, then the continuous version of the population pyramid at time t is given by $\varphi_x(t) = B(t) \cdot e^{-r_i x} \cdot S(x)$, which is a continuous analogue of Equation (6.14b). Taking the derivative with respect to x we find

$$\frac{d}{dx} \varphi_x(t) = B(t) \cdot \left[-r_i \cdot e^{-r_i x} \cdot S(x) - S(x) \cdot \mu_x \cdot e^{-r_i x} \right]$$

$$= -B(t) \cdot e^{-r_i x} \cdot S(x) \cdot (r_i + \mu_x)$$

$$= -B(t) \cdot e^{-r_i x} \cdot e^{-\int_0^x \mu_y \, dy} \cdot (r_i + \mu_x). \qquad \square$$

Example 6.7 shows that a population pyramid can be relatively broader at its base either because r_i is large or because μ_x is large. Conversely, a population pyramid can be relatively narrower in its base either because r_i is small or because μ_x is small. Note that a broad-based pyramid displays a relatively young population, whereas a narrow-based pyramid displays a relatively older population.

The important message of Example 6.7 is that a population can have a large proportion of elderly citizens either because mortality is light (*i.e.*, μ_x is relatively small), or because the rate of births in the population is growing slowly (*i.e.*, r_i is relatively small). This principle is important in funding Social Security systems, as will be seen in Example 6.15 and in Chapter 8.

6.3   APPROXIMATING r_i FROM CENSUS DATA

In the previous section we described the properties of a stable population. Such a population is defined by its constant mortality and fertility profiles, and its intrinsic rates of birth, death, and growth. The relationship of the intrinsic rate of growth to continuous mortality and fertility functions is given by the characteristic equation of the population defined by Equation (6.9). In this model the equation can sometimes be solved explicitly for r_i (see Exercise 6-16).

In practice, however, the mortality and fertility profiles of a population assumed to be stable will be represented by discrete mortality rates from the assumed life table and discrete fertility rates derived from census and vital statistics data, as described in Chapter 2. In this case the characteristic equation yields an approximation of r_i.

Several other approaches to approximating r_i, not using the characteristic equation, will also be explored in this section.

Example 6.8

Show how to approximate the intrinsic rate of increase, given age-and-sex-specific mortality and fertility rates provided by the Vital Statistics Bureau of a particular country.

Solution

First we must modify the characteristic equation given by Equation (6.9) since we are now dealing with discrete data. In this case we will use f_x^f for the age-and-sex-specific fertility rate for mothers aged x last birthday. Instead of the integral expression given by Equation (6.9), we will now use the analogous discrete formula

$$\sum_{\alpha}^{\beta} e^{-r_i y} \cdot S(y) \cdot f_x^f = 1, \qquad (6.15)$$

where y is the average age of the mothers to whom f_x^f applies. Since f_x^f applies to mothers who are age x last birthday, then $x < y < x+1$, and we will generally take $y = x+\frac{1}{2}$. We expand $e^{-r_i y}$ in a Taylor series to obtain

$$\sum S(y) \cdot f_x^f - r_i \sum y \cdot S(y) \cdot f_x^f + \frac{r_i^2}{2} \sum y^2 \cdot S(y) \cdot f_x^f - \cdots = 1. \qquad (6.16)$$

$S(y)$ is the probability of survival from age 0 to age $y = x+\frac{1}{2}$, which is given by $_{x+1/2}p_0 = \dfrac{\ell_{x+1/2}}{\ell_0}$ in life table symbols. Under the uniform distribution of deaths assumption (see Section 3.4.1), $\ell_{x+1/2} = L_x$, so we can substitute $S(y) = \dfrac{L_x}{\ell_0}$ in Equation (6.16). Then with the values of L_x, ℓ_0, and f_x^f available, Equation (6.16) can be truncated after some number of terms and solved by an iterative technique, such as the Newton-Raphson method, for an approximate value of r_i.

If we truncate Equation (6.16) after the r_i^2 term, we obtain the quadratic approximation

$$\frac{\sum L_x f_x^f}{\ell_0} - r_i \frac{\sum (x+\frac{1}{2}) \cdot L_x f_x^f}{\ell_0} + \frac{r_i^2}{2} \frac{\sum (x+\frac{1}{2})^2 \cdot L_x f_x^f}{\ell_0} \approx 1, \qquad (6.17)$$

which can be solved for an approximation to r_i by the quadratic formula.

Another method for approximating r_i begins by recognizing that the factor $\dfrac{\sum L_x f_x^f}{\ell_0}$ in Equation (6.17) is the sex-specific net reproduction rate (NRR) defined in Chapter 2. We define the ratio

$$T = \frac{\sum (x+\frac{1}{2}) \cdot L_x f_x^f}{\sum L_x f_x^f} \qquad (6.18)$$

as the sex-specific *mean length of a generation*. Then $e^{r_i T} \approx$ NRR, since NRR is the ratio of the number in one generation to the number in the preceding generation, which leads to the approximation

$$r_i \approx \frac{\ln(NRR)}{T}. \qquad (6.19)$$

Equation (6.19) can also be derived if we truncate Equation (6.17) after the linear term and use the approximation $1 - \dfrac{1}{NRR} \approx \ln(NRR)$.

Coale (see Keyfitz and Smith [18], pp. 157-160) improved on the approximation given by Equation (6.19) by inputting a fairly standard value of the quadratic term in Equation (6.17) and found

$$r_i \approx \frac{\ln(NRR)}{T - .7 \ln(NRR)}. \qquad (6.20)$$

$\square$

| Example 6.9 |

Calculate the GRR, the NRR, and the mean length of a generation, and approximate the intrinsic rate of increase for the female population described by the following data. Note that quinquennial age groups are used, so some modifications to the developments in Example 6.8 will be required.

Age Group $[x, x+5]$	Number of Females	Central Age $y = x+2\frac{1}{2}$	$S(y)$ L_{x+2}/ℓ_0	Girls Born	$_5f_x^f$
(1)	(2)	(3)	(4)	(5)	(6)
10-15	870,050	12.5	.99043	101	.0001161
15-20	939,600	17.5	.98897	10,362	.0110281
20-25	1,121,895	22.5	.98691	45,412	.0404779
25-30	1,176,520	27.5	.98486	70,021	.0595153
30-35	1,101,880	32.5	.98240	39,844	.0361600
35-40	1,015,120	37.5	.97907	10,812	.0106509
40-45	803,785	42.5	.97381	1,225	.0015240
45-50	655,915	47.5	.96496	44	.0000671
					.1595394

| Solution |

The total of Column (6) multiplied by 5 (for quinquennial age intervals as explained in Section 2.6) is the gross reproduction rate (GRR), so we have

$$GRR = 5 \times .1595394 = .797697.$$

Next we calculate the values shown in the following table.

Age Group	$S(y) \cdot {}_5f_x^f$	$y \cdot S(y) \cdot {}_5f_x^f$	$y^2 \cdot S(y) \cdot {}_5f_x^f$
(1)	(7)	(8)	(9)
10-15	.000114	.0014371	.0179647
15-20	.010906	.1908630	3.3401025
20-25	.039948	.8988319	20.2237180
25-30	.058614	1.6118929	44.3270550
30-35	.035523	1.1545170	37.5218030
35-40	.010428	.3910512	14.6644210
40-45	.001484	.0630753	2.6807004
45-50	.000064	.0030747	.1460500
Total	.157081	4.3147433	122.9218146

Then the total of Column (7) multiplied by 5 is the net reproduction rate (NRR), producing

$$NRR = 5 \times .157081 = .785405.$$

The mean length of a generation, from Equation (6.18), is

$$T = \frac{\text{Column (8)}}{\text{Column (7)}} = 27.46827.$$

Using Equation (6.17), and multiplying each coefficient by 5, we obtain the quadratic

$$.785405 - 21.5737 r_i + 307.3045 r_i^2 = 1,$$

which becomes

$$307.3045 r_i^2 - 21.5737 r_i - .21459 = 0,$$

which solves for $r_i \approx -.8835\%$. With the values $T = 27.46827$, $NRR = .785405$, and with $e^{r_i T} \approx NRR$, we then find

$$r_i \approx \frac{\ln(NRR)}{T} = -.8794\%.$$

Using Coale's approximation we find

$$r_i \approx \frac{\ln(NRR)}{T - .7 \ln(NRR)} = -.8740\%. \qquad \square$$

Since the Canadian female population is not a stable population, the result of $r_i \approx -.88\%$ from Example 6.9 is only an approximation of what the intrinsic growth rate would be if the population approached a stable condition. Note that it is quite different from the *present* crude rate of natural increase, $r_c = +.74\%$, developed in Chapter 2.

Example 6.10

A census has been taken at the midpoint of calendar year z. The population counts are $C_x(z)$ at age x last birthday (so they are approximately age $x+\frac{1}{2}$) and $C_y(z)$ at age y last birthday ($y > x$). It is believed that the population is stable in this age range. Approximate the intrinsic rate of increase r_i.

Solution

$C_x(z)$ derives from a birth cohort $B(z-x)$ and $C_y(z)$ derives from a birth cohort $B(z-y)$. In a stable population with no migration,

$$C_x(z) = B(z-x) \cdot S(x+\tfrac{1}{2}) = B(z) \cdot e^{-r_i x} \cdot S(x+\tfrac{1}{2})$$

and

$$C_y(z) = B(z-y) \cdot S(y+\tfrac{1}{2}) = B(z) \cdot e^{-r_i y} \cdot S(y+\tfrac{1}{2}).$$

Taking the ratio we obtain

$$\frac{C_x(z)}{C_y(z)} = \frac{B(z) \cdot e^{-r_i x} \cdot S(x+\tfrac{1}{2})}{B(z) \cdot e^{-r_i y} \cdot S(y+\tfrac{1}{2})},$$

from which we find $e^{r_i(y-x)} = \dfrac{C_x(z)}{C_y(z)} \cdot \dfrac{S(y+\frac{1}{2})}{S(x+\frac{1}{2})}$. Solving for r_i we have

$$r_i = \left(\frac{1}{y-x}\right) \ln\left[\frac{C_x(z)}{C_y(z)} \cdot \frac{S(y+\frac{1}{2})}{S(x+\frac{1}{2})}\right] \tag{6.21a}$$

$$= \left(\frac{1}{y-x}\right) \ln\left[\frac{C_x(z)}{C_y(z)} \cdot \frac{L_y}{L_x}\right], \tag{6.21b}$$

where $S(x+\frac{1}{2}) = \dfrac{L_x}{\ell_0}$ and $S(y+\frac{1}{2}) = \dfrac{L_y}{\ell_0}$ under the uniform distribution of deaths assumption, so $\dfrac{S(y+\frac{1}{2})}{S(x+\frac{1}{2})} = \dfrac{L_y}{L_x}.$ □

Example 6.11

A woman gave birth to a daughter at age 23 and another at age 30. We are given that $S(23) = .95$ and $S(30) = .93$. What is the intrinsic rate of increase in a population in which all women who survive have this childbearing pattern?

Solution

If all women in the population have this childbearing pattern, then $f_{23}^f = f_{30}^f = 1$, and $f_x^f = 0$ for all other x. Then the discrete form of the characteristic equation, given by Equation (6.15), becomes $e^{-23r_i} \cdot S(23) + e^{-30r_i} \cdot S(30) = 1$, which is then solved for r_i using an iterative method. (The reader is referred to Exercise 6-11, where the mother gives birth at ages 20 and 40. The latter problem lends itself to an easy algebraic solution.) □

Example 6.12

What is the average age at death of those dying in a particular year in a stable population with a constant force of mortality μ, and a constant intrinsic rate of increase r_i? Compare this with the age to which a randomly chosen newborn can expect to live.

Solution

For a randomly chosen newborn, the expected age at death is given by Equation (3.23) as $\overset{\circ}{e}_0 = \int_0^\infty {}_tp_0 \, dt$. With a constant force of mortality we have $\overset{\circ}{e}_0 = \int_0^\infty e^{-\mu t} \, dt = -\frac{1}{\mu} \cdot e^{-\mu t} \Big|_0^\infty = \frac{1}{\mu}$. In a stable population, the average age at death of those dying in a particular year is

$$\frac{\int_0^\infty x \cdot e^{-r_i x} \cdot S(x) \cdot \mu_x \, dx}{\int_0^\infty e^{-r_i x} \cdot S(x) \cdot \mu_x \, dx} = \frac{\int_0^\infty x \cdot e^{-r_i x} \cdot e^{-\mu x} \cdot \mu \, dx}{\int_0^\infty e^{-r_i x} \cdot e^{-\mu x} \cdot \mu \, dx}$$

$$= \frac{\int_0^\infty x \cdot e^{-(r_i+\mu)x} \, dx}{\int_0^\infty e^{-(r_i+\mu)x} \, dx}.$$

Integrating we obtain

$$\frac{-\left(\frac{1}{r_i+\mu}\right)^2 e^{-(r_i+\mu)x} \Big|_0^\infty}{-\left(\frac{1}{r_i+\mu}\right) e^{-(r_i+\mu)x} \Big|_0^\infty} = \frac{1}{r_i + \mu}. \qquad □$$

Example 6.12 shows us that if $r_i > 0$, the average age at death in the population is less than $\overset{\circ}{e}_0$, the average age at death for newborn lives. The converse is true if $r_i < 0$. If $r_i = 0$, we have a stationary population and the two concepts are numerically equal.

| Example 6.13 |

Compare the average attained age in a stable population, with intrinsic rate of growth r_i, with that in the associated stationary population, which has $r_i = 0$, but has the same mortality profile.

| Solution |

The average attained age of an entire stationary population is

$$\bar{x} = \frac{\int_0^\infty x \cdot \ell_x \, dx}{\int_0^\infty \ell_x \, dx}.$$

For a stable population we have

$$\bar{x} = \frac{\int_0^\infty x \cdot e^{-r_i x} \cdot S(x) \, dx}{\int_0^\infty e^{-r_i x} \cdot S(x) \, dx}.$$

If we assume a continuous function for $S(x)$, such as $S(x) = e^{-\mu x}$ under the assumption $\mu_x = \mu$ for all x, then we can solve directly for a numerical value of $\bar{x}$. If our mortality profile is given by a discrete life table, instead of a continuous survival function, then we must resort to approximation techniques. Expanding $e^{-r_i x}$ in a series we have

$$\bar{x} \approx \frac{\int_0^\infty x(1 - r_i x + \frac{r_i^2}{2} x^2) \cdot S(x) \, dx}{\int_0^\infty (1 - r_i x + \frac{r_i^2}{2} x^2) \cdot S(x) \, dx} = \frac{Q_1 - r_i \cdot Q_2 + \frac{r_i^2}{2} \cdot Q_3}{Q_0 - r_i \cdot Q_1 + \frac{r_i^2}{2} \cdot Q_2},$$

where $Q_i = \int_0^\infty x^i \cdot S(x) \, dx$ is the numerator of the ith moment about zero of the age distribution in the stationary population described by the associated life table. Long division gives us

$$\bar{x} \approx \frac{Q_1}{Q_0} - r_i \left[\frac{Q_2}{Q_0} - \left(\frac{Q_1}{Q_0} \right)^2 \right] = \frac{Q_1}{Q_0} - r_i \cdot \sigma^2,$$

where $\dfrac{Q_1}{Q_0}$ is the mean, and σ^2 is the variance, of the age distribution in the stationary population described by the associated life table. Note that if $r_i = 0$, then $\bar{x} = \dfrac{Q_1}{Q_0}$, the same value for the mean. If $r_i > 0$, then $\bar{x} < \dfrac{Q_1}{Q_0}$, and if $r_i < 0$, then $\bar{x} > \dfrac{Q_1}{Q_0}$. Finally we can write

$$r_i \approx \frac{\dfrac{Q_1}{Q_0} - \bar{x}}{\sigma^2},$$

which gives us another approximation for r_i, if $\bar{x}$ were given. $\qquad\square$

6.4 APPLICATIONS

If a population can be modeled using stable population theory, many interesting applications are possible. The following five examples illustrate some of these applications.

Example 6.14

Let k be the ratio of employees above age x to those below age x. k is therefore a measure of seniority, and possibly a measure of the likelihood of promotion. If μ_x is constant for $\alpha < x < \beta$, the range of ages of employment, find an expression for k.

Solution

Since $\mu_x = \mu$, a constant, then $S(x) = e^{-\mu x}$, so we have

$$k = \frac{\int_x^\beta e^{-r_i y} \cdot e^{-\mu y}\, dy}{\int_\alpha^x e^{-r_i y} \cdot e^{-\mu y}\, dy} = \frac{e^{-(r_i+\mu)x} - e^{-(r_i+\mu)\beta}}{e^{-(r_i+\mu)\alpha} - e^{-(r_i+\mu)x}}.$$

Solving for x we find

$$x = -\frac{1}{r_i+\mu} \ln\left[\frac{k \cdot e^{-(r_i+\mu)\alpha} + e^{-(r_i+\mu)\beta}}{k+1}\right].$$

Note that $\dfrac{dk}{dr_i} = \dfrac{dk}{d\mu}$, which shows that r_i and μ have the same impact on promotions. $\qquad\square$

Example 6.15

A population is stable with intrinsic growth rate r_i, and constant force of mortality μ_x for all x. Determine the *pension burden*, which is the ratio of the population over age 65 to that aged 20 to 65.

Solution

The pension burden is $\dfrac{\int_{65}^{\infty} \ell_x \, dx}{\int_{20}^{65} \ell_x \, dx} = \dfrac{T_{65}}{T_{20} - T_{65}}$ in a stationary

population. In a stable population it is $\dfrac{\int_{65}^{\infty} e^{-r_i x} \cdot S(x) \, dx}{\int_{20}^{65} e^{-r_i x} \cdot S(x) \, dx}$. If μ is

constant for all ages, then $S(x) = e^{-\mu x}$, and the pension burden is

$$\frac{\int_{65}^{\infty} e^{-r_i x} \cdot e^{-\mu x} \, dx}{\int_{20}^{65} e^{-r_i x} \cdot e^{-\mu x} \, dx} = \frac{\int_{65}^{\infty} e^{-(r_i + \mu)x} \, dx}{\int_{20}^{65} e^{-(r_i + \mu)x} \, dx}$$

$$= \frac{-\left(\dfrac{1}{r_i + \mu}\right) e^{-(r_i + \mu)x} \Big|_{65}^{\infty}}{-\left(\dfrac{1}{r_i + \mu}\right) e^{-(r_i + \mu)x} \Big|_{20}^{65}}$$

$$= \frac{e^{-65(r_i + \mu)}}{e^{-20(r_i + \mu)} - e^{-65(r_i + \mu)}}.$$

We need only values for r_i and μ to complete the calculation. For example, if $r_i = .01$ and $\mu = .015$, the resulting pension burden is .48, or approximately two potential workers per retiree. In a stationary population with the same mortality profile, $r_i = 0$ and the pension burden is $\dfrac{e^{-65\mu}}{e^{-20\mu} - e^{-65\mu}}$, which, for $\mu = .015$, evaluates to 1.037, or more than one retiree per worker.   □

Example 6.16

Using the expression for the pension burden in a stable population given in Example 6.15, show that $\dfrac{d}{dr_i} \ln(PB) = \bar{x}_1 - \bar{x}_2$, where $\bar{x}_1$ is the average age of those aged 20 to 65 at time t, and $\bar{x}_2$ is the average age of those aged 65 and over at time t.

Solution

$$\frac{d}{dr_i}\ln(PB) = \frac{d}{dr_i}\left[\ln\int_{65}^{\infty}e^{-r_ix}\cdot S(x)\,dx\right] - \frac{d}{dr_i}\left[\ln\int_{20}^{65}e^{-r_ix}\cdot S(x)\,dx\right]$$

$$= \frac{-\int_{65}^{\infty}x\cdot e^{-r_ix}\cdot S(x)\,dx}{\int_{65}^{\infty}e^{-r_ix}\cdot S(x)\,dx} - \frac{-\int_{20}^{65}x\cdot e^{-r_ix}\cdot S(x)\,dx}{\int_{20}^{65}e^{-r_ix}\cdot S(x)\,dx}$$

$$= -\bar{x}_2 - (-\bar{x}_1) = \bar{x}_1 - \bar{x}_2.$$

(See Example 8.2 for an application of this result.) □

Example 6.17

(a) A country's social insurance system pays a dollar at the death of each citizen aged 20 to 65. Find the pay-as-you-go assessment for this benefit, π, to be paid by all citizens aged 20 to 65, if the population is stable.

(b) What is π if the population is stationary?

Solution

(a) The value of the benefits is $\int_{20}^{65} e^{-r_ix}\cdot S(x)\cdot\mu_x\,dx$, and the value of the assessment income is $\pi\int_{20}^{65} e^{-r_ix}\cdot S(x)\,dx$. Thus we have

$$\pi = \frac{\int_{20}^{65} e^{-r_ix}\cdot S(x)\cdot\mu_x\,dx}{\int_{20}^{65} e^{-r_ix}\cdot S(x)\,dx}.$$

(b) If the population is stationary, then $r_i = 0$ and the expression for π reduces to

$$\pi = \frac{\int_{20}^{65}\ell_x\mu_x\,dx}{\int_{20}^{65}\ell_x\,dx} = \frac{-\ell_x\big|_{20}^{65}}{-T_x\big|_{20}^{65}} = \frac{\ell_{20}-\ell_{65}}{T_{20}-T_{65}}. \qquad \square$$

Example 6.18

(a) If a population starts at one birth per year at time 0 (*i.e.*, $B(0) = 1$), and grows at rate r_i, show that t years later (such that $r_i t$ is large) the annual rate of births in the population is $B(t) = e^{r_i t}$ and the number of people who have ever lived is approximately $\frac{e^{r_i t}}{r_i}$.

(b)   Show that the fraction of the number of people who have ever lived who are still alive at time t is approximately $\frac{r_i}{b_i}$, where b_i is the intrinsic birth rate of the population introduced in Section 6.2.

[Solution]

(a) $B(t) = B(0) \cdot e^{r_i t}$ and $B(0) = 1$, so $B(t) = e^{r_i t}$. The total number who have ever lived is the total ever born, which, since $B(0) = 1$, is given by

$$\int_0^t e^{r_i s} ds = \frac{1}{r_i} \cdot e^{r_i s} \Big|_0^t = \frac{e^{r_i t} - 1}{r_i} \approx \frac{e^{r_i t}}{r_i},$$

if $r_i t$ is large.

(b) $b_i = \frac{B(t)}{P(t)} = \frac{e^{r_i t}}{\text{number alive at time } t}$, so the number alive at time t is $\frac{e^{r_i t}}{b_i}$. The number who have ever lived is nearly $\frac{e^{r_i t}}{r_i}$, so the fraction still alive is nearly $\frac{e^{r_i t}/b_i}{e^{r_i t}/r_i} = \frac{r_i}{b_i}$.   □

6.5 QUASI-STABLE POPULATIONS

Recall that a stationary population model has a constant annual rate of births and a constant mortality profile over time. In moving on to the stable population model, we let the annual rate at which births were occurring in the population change by a force of growth r_i, and we saw that this same value of r_i was the force of growth in the population itself. This dual role of r_i is expressed in Equations (6.3) and (6.4).

Now suppose a population continues to experience a force of growth in its annual rate of births, and, as well, experiences a change in its mortality profile over time. Such a population is called a *quasi-stable population*. Without loss of generality, let us assume that mortality is *improving* over time, as indicated by a declining force of mortality at all ages over time. Intuitively we can see that in this case the population grows from *both* the increasing births *and* the declining mortality, so the force of growth of the population itself is *greater* than the force of growth in the annual rate of births. Since these two forces of growth are not equal we must have different symbols for them.

We denote the force of growth in the annual rate of births by r_i^b, so Equation (6.3) becomes

$$B(t+n) \ = \ B(t) \cdot e^{n \cdot r_i^b}, \tag{6.3a}$$

and similarly we denote the force of growth in the population itself by r_i^p, so Equation (6.4) becomes

$$P(t+n) \ = \ P(t) \cdot e^{n \cdot r_i^p}. \tag{6.4a}$$

To summarize, in a stable population $r_i^b = r_i^p = r_i$, whereas in a quasi-stable population $r_i^p > r_i^b$ if mortality is improving (μ_x is declining) over time, and $r_i^p < r_i^b$ if mortality is worsening (μ_x is increasing) over time.

Next we must quantify the idea of mortality improving over time. Suppose the population experiences an improvement in its mortality profile measured by a constant reduction in the force of mortality over time. Let $\mu_u(a)$ and $\mu_u(a+t)$ denote the continuous mortality profiles applicable to persons born in year a, and year $a+t$, respectively, and let $\mu_u(a+t) = \mu_u(a) - kt$ for all u.

Therefore we can say that a quasi-stable population is defined by its force of growth in the annual rate of births r_i^b, its *initial* mortality profile $\mu_u(a)$, and its mortality improvement factor k. Given these three parameters the force of growth for the population itself, denoted by r_i^p, can be obtained.

Conversely, if we have information about the population's growth revealed through a census, and we assume the mortality improvement pattern described above, then we can find the intrinsic force of growth in the rate of births that would lead to the observed population growth. This is pursued in the following example, which is the extension of Example 6.10 to the quasi-stable case.

Example 6.19

Derive an expression for the force of growth in the rate of births in a quasi-stable population, denoted by r_i^b, given census counts of $C_x(z)$ and $C_y(z)$ at ages x and y last birthday, respectively, where $y > x$. Let $t = y - x$. Let the continuous mortality profile applicable to the birth cohort whose survivors are age y last birthday at the time of the calendar year z census be denoted by $\mu_u(a)$, and similarly let $\mu_u(a+t)$ denote the continuous mortality profile applicable to the birth cohort whose survivors are age x last birthday. Assume that $\mu_u(a+t) = \mu_u(a) - kt = \mu_u(a) - k(y-x)$ for all u. Finally, assume that those age x and y last birthday are, on average, age $x+\frac{1}{2}$ and $y+\frac{1}{2}$, respectively, when the census is taken. Note that $t = y - x = (y+\frac{1}{2}) - (x+\frac{1}{2})$.

Solution

If $B(z)$ denotes the annual birth rate at the time of the census in year z, then we know that

$$C_x(z) = B(z) \cdot e^{-r_i^b x} \cdot S_{a+t}(x+\tfrac{1}{2})$$

and

$$C_y(z) = B(z) \cdot e^{-r_i^b y} \cdot S_a(y+\tfrac{1}{2}).$$

Recall that

$$S_a(y+\tfrac{1}{2}) = exp\left[-\int_0^{y+1/2} \mu_u(a)\, du \right]$$

and

$$S_{a+t}(x+\tfrac{1}{2}) = exp\left[-\int_0^{x+1/2} \mu_u(a+t)\, du \right]$$

$$= exp\left[-\int_0^{x+1/2} [\mu_u(a) - kt]\, du \right]$$

$$= S_a(x+\tfrac{1}{2}) \cdot e^{kt(x+1/2)}.$$

Substituting this expression for $S_{a+t}(x+\tfrac{1}{2})$ and taking the ratio of $C_x(z)$ to $C_y(z)$ we obtain

$$\frac{C_x(z)}{C_y(z)} = \frac{B(z) \cdot e^{-r_i^b x} \cdot S_a(x+\tfrac{1}{2}) \cdot e^{kt(x+1/2)}}{B(z) \cdot e^{-r_i^b y} \cdot S_a(y+\tfrac{1}{2})}$$

$$= e^{r_i^b(y-x)} \cdot \frac{S_a(x+\tfrac{1}{2})}{S_a(y+\tfrac{1}{2})} \cdot e^{k(x+1/2)(y-x)},$$

by cancelling the $B(z)$ terms and substituting $t = y - x$. Finally we note that $\dfrac{S_a(x+\frac{1}{2})}{S_a(y+\frac{1}{2})} = \dfrac{L_x^a}{L_y^a}$, where L_x^a and L_y^a are taken from the life table based on the continuous mortality profile defined by $\mu_u(a)$. Then we can solve for r_i^b, obtaining

$$e^{r_i^b(y-x)} = \frac{C_x(z)}{C_y(z)} \cdot \frac{L_y^a}{L_x^a} \cdot e^{-k(x+1/2)(y-x)},$$

so that

$$r_i^b = \frac{1}{y-x}\left[\ln\left(\frac{C_x(z)}{C_y(z)} \cdot \frac{L_y^a}{L_x^a} \cdot e^{-k(x+1/2)(y-x)}\right)\right]$$

$$= \frac{1}{y-x}\left[\ln\left(\frac{C_x(z)}{C_y(z)} \cdot \frac{L_y^a}{L_x^a}\right)\right] - k(x+\tfrac{1}{2})$$

$$= r_i - k(x+\tfrac{1}{2}),$$

where $r_i = \dfrac{1}{y-x}\left[\ln\left(\dfrac{C_x(z)}{C_y(z)} \cdot \dfrac{L_y^a}{L_x^a}\right)\right]$ is the value of r_i^b (and of r_i^p as well) if the population were stable (see Example 6.10), since, in that case, $k = 0$. $\qquad \Box$

6.6 EXERCISES

6.1 Introduction;
6.2 The Foundations of Stable Population Theory

6-1. In a country where $r_i = .005$ and $\mu_x = .015$ for all x, determine the ratio of the number of person-years lived in the year in which the country has 1000 births, to the total future lifetime of the 1000 births.

6-2. The population of a certain country is growing at rate of increase $r_i = .005$. If $\mu_x = .015$ for all x, find the absolute value of the difference between the average age of all deaths in the country in one year, and $\overset{\circ}{e}_0$, the life expectancy for a newborn in the country.

6-3.   (a) In a country where $r_i = .01$ and $d_i = .015$, find b_i, the intrinsic birth rate for the population.

(b) The result in part (a) measures the average number of births per year per member of the population. Alternatively, find the average number of births per member of a particular birth cohort, assuming $\mu_x = .015$ for all x.

6-4.   Show that $\frac{d}{dt} P(t) = B(t) - D(t)$.

6-5.   Given a stable population with $r_i = 2\%$ and $b_i = 3.5\%$, calculate μ if $\mu_x = \mu$ for all x.

6-6.   If $r_i = 1\%$ and $S(x) = (1 - \frac{x}{100})$, $0 < x < 100$, find the intrinsic death rate d_i.

6-7.   Calculate the population at age 50 nearest birthday for a stable population, given the following information.

(i)   The population is increasing at an intrinsic rate of 2%.
(ii) $_{40}p_0 = .8$ and $_{50}p_0 = .7$
(iii) The population at age 40 nearest birthday is 10,000.

6-8.   In Canada the English-speaking population is in a stationary condition $(r_i = 0)$ with $\mu_x = .015$ for all x. The French-speaking population has a stable population with $r_i = .005$ and $\mu_x = .010$ for all x. Find the ratio of the Anglophone intrinsic birth rate b_i to the Francophone intrinsic birth rate b_i'.

6-9.   The State of Mississippi has two numerically equal subpopulations, black and white, both stable and growing at the rate of increase $r_i = 1\%$, but with different life tables. A medical cure is found for sickle cell anemia, which drops the force of mortality for the black population from $\mu_x^B = .015$ to .014 for all x. For the white population $\mu_x^W = .011$ for all x. Before the cure was found, the intrinsic death rate for the entire population was $d_i = .013$. What is the intrinsic death rate for the entire population 100 years after the medical cure?

6.3 Approximating r_i from Census Data

6-10. The values of female mortality and female age-and-sex-specific fertility are as follows for a certain animal species.

x	q_x	f_x^f
0	.4	0
1	.1	1
2	.2	3
3	.5	2
4	1.0	0

Assuming a uniform distribution of events, calculate (a) the gross reproduction rate, (b) the net reproduction rate, and (c) the mean length of a generation.

6-11. A woman gives birth to a daughter at age 20 and another at age 40. Given $S(20) = .96$ and $S(40) = .90$, find the intrinsic rate of increase in a population in which all women who survive have exactly this childbearing pattern.

6-12. In a population the census count for males was 1314 at ages 25-30 and 538 at ages 50-55. The values $L_{27} = 408$ and $L_{52} = 351$ are found in the applicable life table. Find the rate of increase r_i for the population, assuming stability.

6-13. Given a net reproduction rate of 1.353 and mean length of generation 27.31, determine (a) Coale's approximation for r_i, and (b) the value that would be determined using a first order approximation without Coale's improvement factor.

6-14. For a particular population, Coale's approximation yields $r_i \approx 1\%$. It is also known that the net reproduction rate is such that $\ln(\text{NRR}) = .3$. Find the mean length of a generation for this population.

6-15. You are given the following information for U.S. females.

Age Group $[x, x+5)$	Central Age $y = x+2\frac{1}{2}$	$\dfrac{L_{x+2}}{\ell_0}$	$_5f_x^f$
10-15	12.5	.9730	.0004
15-20	17.5	.9710	.0356
20-25	22.5	.9679	.1074
25-30	27.5	.9641	.0877
30-35	32.5	.9590	.0507
35-40	37.5	.9516	.0244
40-45	42.5	.9408	.0068
45-50	47.5	.9248	.0004

(a) Find the net reproduction rate.
(b) Find the mean length of a generation.
(c) Approximate the intrinsic rate of increase r_i, using Coale's approximation.

6-16. Determine the intrinsic rate of increase for a stable population, given the following information. (Hint: $\int_0^\infty x^{\alpha-1} e^{-\beta x}\, dx = (\alpha-1)!\,\beta^{-\alpha}$, for each integer $\alpha \geq 1$.)

(i) $\mu_x = .02$, for $x \geq 0$.
(ii) The age-and-sex-specific fertility function is given by
$\phi_x^f = x^3 \cdot e^{-.8x},\ 0 \leq x < \infty$.

6-17. For a certain stable population, the census count at age 20 was 235,000 and at age 80 it was 35,000. The applicable life table gives $L_0 = 99{,}000$, $L_{20} = 85{,}000$ and $L_{80} = 15{,}000$.

(a) Approximate the intrinsic rate of increase r_i.
(b) It is discovered that the force of mortality underlying the applicable life table was understated by .0005 at every age. Recalculate the intrinsic rate of increase.

6-18. From the life table applicable to a stable population we find the values $\dfrac{Q_1}{Q_0} = 37.36$ and $\sigma^2 = 539.04$. Furthermore, it is known that $\bar{x} = 22.32$. Approximate r_i.

6-19. For a stable population, the following information is given.

   (i) $r_i = .01$
   (ii) $\mu_x = .01$ for all ages through the end of the childbearing period.
   (iii) The fertility function is $\phi_x^f = k \cdot e^{-.02x}$, $25 \leq x \leq 50$, and zero elsewhere.

   Determine k.

6-20. Assume the following information for a stable animal population.

   (i)   The population is increasing at an intrinsic growth rate of $r_i = .10$.
   (ii) Mortality is given by the following table.

x	ℓ_x
0	1000
1	800
2	300
3	0

   (iii) All deaths occur at exact ages .5, 1.5, or 2.5.

   Determine the average age at death of the population.

6-21. You are given separate stable populations, one for males in which the force of mortality is .015 at all ages and the intrinsic rate of increase is 1.95% per year, and one for females in which $S(x) = 1 - x/100$ and the intrinsic rate of increase is 2%. The ratio of males to females at birth is 52/50 at the present time. Find the sex ratio for persons presently aged 60.

6.4 Applications

6-22. Given a stable population with parameters $\mu_x = .02$ for all x and $r_i = .01$, determine the pension burden at any time.

6-23. If $r_i = 1\%$ and $S(x) = 1 - \frac{x}{100}$, $x \leq 100$, for a retirement community that people enter at age 65, find the intrinsic death rate in the retirement community.

6-24. G.M. Corporation started in 1920 by hiring 200 employees. In 1985 it hired 3000 new employees.

(a) If new entrants grew exponentially during that time, how many people worked for G.M. during that period? Assume no one was ever hired twice.

(b) Answer part (a) assuming an arithmetic increase in new entrants.

6-25. In a certain country the intrinsic birth rate is 15 per 1000 and the population is doubling every 100 years. What fraction of the population that ever lived is alive at any time? (Use standard approximations.)

6-26. In North America the number of Fellows of the Society of Actuaries has been increasing for a long time at intrinsic rate $r_i = .03$ (net of new Fellows less deaths and withdrawals). Each year the number of new Fellows is 5% of the number of existing Fellows. What percentage of Fellows who have ever existed are alive at any given moment?

6-27. The number of Honours Actuarial Science students at the University of Toronto has been increasing for a long time at intrinsic rate 2% (entrants less dropouts and graduates). Each year the number of new entrants is $1/3$ of the number present. Approximately what fraction of the Honours Actuarial Science students who have ever existed at the University of Toronto are now on campus?

6-28. The pension burden is defined as $PB = \dfrac{\int_{65}^{\infty} e^{-r_i x} \cdot S(x)\, dx}{\int_{20}^{65} e^{-r_i x} \cdot S(x)\, dx}$, and you are given $r_i = .01$ and $\mu_x = .02$ for all x. Find $\dfrac{d}{dr_i} \ln(PB)$.

6-29. Given an annual rate of births at time t of $B(t) = 1000e^{.01t}$ and a survival function of $S(x) = e^{-.01x}$, determine the annual assessment π to be paid by all citizens aged 20 and over to fund a scheme to pay a dollar at the death of any citizen.

6-30. For a stable population you are given (i) the force of mortality is constant, and (ii) the median age is 50. Determine the proportion of the population that is under age 100.

6-31. A stable population has been growing at the intrinsic rate $r_i = 1\%$ for a long time. The annual rate of births reaches $B(t) = 200,000$ on January 1, 1990. Assuming babies are born at a constant number of 200,000 per year after this date, project the total size of the population on January 1, 2011, if the force of mortality is .008 at all ages.

6-32. A company's active employee group is growing at intrinsic rate $r_i = 2\%$. Workers are hired at age 25 and retire at age 65. If $\mu_x = .015$ how many years of pension credits are amassed the year that there are 200 workers hired at age 25?

6-33. If there were 1000 births in a population in the year 1700 and 40,000 in the year 1950, find the total number of births between 1700 and 1950, assuming an exponential increase.

6.5 Quasi-Stable Populations

6-34. For a certain stable population, the census count was 300,000 at age 25 and 200,000 at age 50. The appropriate life table shows $L_{25} = 95,000$ and $L_{50} = 85,000$.

(a) Approximate the intrinsic rate of increase r_i.
(b) If the population were quasi-stable with an improvement in the force of mortality between successive annual cohorts of $k = .0002$ per year, as described in Example 6.19, approximate r_i^b, the force of growth in the annual rate of births.

6-35. Find the value of r_i^p, the force of growth in the population itself, for the quasi-stable population described in part (b) of Exercise 6-34.

CHAPTER 7

POPULATION PROJECTIONS

7.1 INTER-CENSAL AND IMMEDIATE POST-CENSAL ESTIMATES

Most industrialized nations take a major census every ten years. Many countries, including Canada, take a mini-census halfway between the major censuses. At these points very careful tabulations are made of the population (see Chapter 1). If a demographer wishes to estimate the total population, ignoring any breakdown by age, sex, or other demographic parameters, between censuses or immediately after a census, a number of basic mathematical techniques is available.

7.1.1 Linear Interpolation

Given census data at time 0, $P(0)$, and at time n, $P(n)$, the estimated population at time t, $0 \leq t \leq n$, using linear interpolation is given by

$$P(t) = \left(1 - \tfrac{t}{n}\right) \cdot P(0) + \tfrac{t}{n} \cdot P(n) \qquad (7.1a)$$

$$= P(0) + \tfrac{t}{n}[P(n) - P(0)]. \qquad (7.1b)$$

The demographer who uses this formula is assuming that the population is growing linearly. These equations can also be used for linear extrapolation (*i.e.*, $t > n$) to estimate the population count after the last census, assuming the linear pattern of growth from $t = 0$ to $t = n$ continues to hold. Linear extrapolation should not be used for large values of t (*e.g.*, $t > 2n$) unless the assumption of linear growth is truly believed to hold.

7.1.2 Polynomial Interpolation

Given $n+1$ historic data values $P(0)$, $P(1)$, $P(2)$, $\cdots$, $P(n)$, a polynomial of degree n can be fit to these points that will reproduce all of the given values. Such a polynomial can then be used to estimate values of $P(t)$ which are between or beyond the given data points. Such a method should be used with care, especially for large values of n (higher degree polynomials) and extrapolated estimates. A polynomial of degree $n > 2$ can be very unpredictable, so that extrapolated values, and sometimes interpolated values, can turn out to be absurd. Therefore this method is not popular among demographers.

7.1.3 Geometric Modeling

Reference has already been made to population growth models of the form

$$P(t) \;=\; P(0){\cdot}(1+r_a)^t, \tag{7.2a}$$

where r_a is an annual effective rate, or

$$P(t) \;=\; P(0){\cdot}e^{r_i t}, \tag{7.2b}$$

where r_i is a continuous instantaneous growth rate.[1]

The derivation of the value of r_i as a force of growth operating in a stable population received extensive discussion in Chapter 6. However, for inter-censal or immediate post-censal estimates, growth rates can be more simply derived. For example, given two census counts n years apart, $P(0)$ and $P(n)$, the effective annual growth rate implied by these values is obtained from $P(n) = P(0){\cdot}(1+r_a)^n$, so that

$$r_a \;=\; \left(\frac{P(n)}{P(0)}\right)^{\frac{1}{n}} - 1. \tag{7.3a}$$

Alternatively we can use $P(n) = P(0){\cdot}e^{r_i n}$, obtaining

$$r_i \;=\; \tfrac{1}{n}{\cdot}\ln\left(\frac{P(n)}{P(0)}\right) \;=\; \ln(1+r_a) \tag{7.3b}$$

---

[1]In interest theory, the continuous instantaneous growth rate for a fund of money is called the force of interest. In this text we will occasionally refer to our continuous instantaneous population growth rate as the force of growth.

as a continuous instantaneous growth rate. Having derived an estimated growth rate that reflects the short-term growth pattern, unknown values of $P(t)$ can then be estimated using either of Equations (7.2).

This is a very popular method for finding interpolated values and short-term extrapolated values.

| Example 7.1 |

Given the July 1 U.S. data $P(70) = 203.2$ million and $P(80) = 226.5$ million, estimate the population on July 1, 1978 and July 1, 1989, assuming (a) linear growth, (b) effective annual growth rate of r_a, and (c) a continuous instantaneous growth rate of r_i.

| Solution |

(a) Using Formula (7.1a),

$$P(78) = \frac{2}{10}P(70) + \frac{8}{10}P(80)$$

$$= P(70) + \frac{8}{10}\Big(P(80) - P(70)\Big)$$

$$= 221.8.$$

Assuming constant linear growth, we can use Equation (7.1b) to find

$$P(89) = P(70) + \frac{19}{10}\Big(P(80) - P(70)\Big) = 247.5.$$

(b) To find r_a we let $P(80) = P(70)\cdot(1+r_a)^{10}$, from which we obtain $r_a = \left(\frac{226.5}{203.2}\right)^{\frac{1}{10}} - 1 = 1.09145\%$. Then

$$P(78) = P(70)\cdot(1+r_a)^8 = 221.6$$

and

$$P(89) = P(70)\cdot(1+r_a)^{19} = 249.7.$$

Alternatively, we can obtain $P(89)$ from $P(80)$ as

$$P(89) = P(80)\cdot(1+r_a)^9 = 249.7.$$

(c)   To find r_i we let $P(80) = P(70) \cdot e^{10r_i}$, from which we find
$r_i = \frac{1}{10} \cdot \ln\left(\frac{226.5}{203.2}\right) = 1.08554\%$. Then

$$P(78) = P(70) \cdot e^{8r_i} = 221.6$$

and

$$P(89) = P(70) \cdot e^{19r_i} = P(80) \cdot e^{9r_i} = 249.7. \qquad \square$$

The relationship between the linear growth model (L) and the geometric growth model (G) is

$$P_L(78) > P_G(78) \tag{7.4a}$$

and

$$P_L(89) < P_G(89). \tag{7.4b}$$

This is illustrated in the following figure, where both models are designed to reproduce the 1970 and 1980 populations.

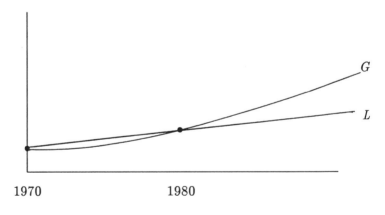

FIGURE 7.1

The models given by Equations (7.2a) and (7.2b) imply the same geometric growth pattern. They are really just two different forms of the same model, connected by the relationship $r_i = \ln(1 + r_a)$. Thus they are identical, and will give identical estimates for all t, as shown by Example 7.1.

| Example 7.2 |

Develop a rule of thumb to approximate the time required for a population to double in size, given a force of growth r_i.

| Solution |

The equation that represents the time for doubling is $P \cdot e^{r_i t} = 2P$, or simply $e^{r_i t} = 2$. Then we have $r_i t = \ln 2 = .693$, and $t = \frac{.693}{r_i}$. This is commonly approximated as $t \approx \frac{70}{100 r_i}$. For example, if a population is growing at 2% per year, then it will take approximately 35 years for that population to double. $\qquad\square$

7.2 POPULATION PROJECTIONS: THE LOGISTIC CURVE

All of the methods described in the previous section have no upper bound on growth, which is a significant deficiency. For example, the growth models illustrated in Example 7.1 all lead to an infinitely large population if projected to $t = \infty$.

A model that sets an upper bound on the ultimate population was first postulated by Verhulst (see Keyfitz and Smith [18], pp. 333-338) in 1838 and is known as the *logistic model*. (See Figure 7.2.)

A continuous instantaneous population growth rate r_t is defined by

$$r_t = \frac{1}{P(t)} \cdot \frac{dP(t)}{dt}, \qquad (7.5)$$

where, in general, r_t is a function of t. In the special case where r_t is constant over time, and equal to r_i, then Equation (7.2b) results.[2] However the logistic model sets an upper bound on growth, such that $\lim_{t \to \infty} P(t) = a$. To reach an upper bound, it is clear that the instantaneous growth rate r_t must decrease over time, and eventually reach zero.

---

[2]The reader familiar with compound interest theory will recognize that r_t is analogous to the varying force of interest δ_t. If $\delta_t = \delta$, a constant, then the accumulated value at time t of an amount $A(0)$ invested at time 0 is $A(t) = A(0) \cdot e^{\delta t}$, which is analogous to Equation (7.2b).

We begin with the differential equation

$$\frac{1}{P(t)} \cdot \frac{dP(t)}{dt} = r_t = k\left[1 - \frac{P(t)}{a}\right], \qquad (7.6)$$

which is analogous to Equation (7.5), but with the required decreasing pattern for the instantaneous growth rate. Note that as $t \to \infty$, $P(t) \to a$, so $r_t \to 0$ as required. Note also that at $t=0$, we have $r_0 = k\left[1 - \frac{P(0)}{a}\right] \neq k$, since $P(0) \neq 0$. Therefore it is not correct to interpret k as the initial growth rate at time 0; k, like a, is simply a parameter of the model that must be specified.

To solve Equation (7.6) for $P(t)$, we rearrange it to obtain

$$\frac{dP}{P\left(1 - \frac{P}{a}\right)} = k \cdot dt, \qquad (7.7a)$$

where P is used in place of $P(t)$ for notational convenience. Breaking the left side into partial fractions, we have

$$\left[\frac{\frac{1}{a}}{1 - \frac{P}{a}} + \frac{1}{P}\right] dP = k \cdot dt. \qquad (7.7b)$$

Next we integrate both sides of (7.7b) to obtain

$$-\ln\left[1 - \frac{P}{a}\right] + \ln P = kt + c, \qquad (7.7c)$$

or

$$\ln\left[\frac{P}{1 - \frac{P}{a}}\right] = kt + c. \qquad (7.7d)$$

Evaluating Equation (7.7d) at $t = 0$, we find the constant of integration

$$c = \ln\left[\frac{P(0)}{1 - \frac{P(0)}{a}}\right], \qquad (7.7\text{e})$$

which, when substituted into (7.7d), gives us

$$\ln\left[\frac{P(t)}{1 - \frac{P(t)}{a}}\right] = kt + \ln\left[\frac{P(0)}{1 - \frac{P(0)}{a}}\right], \qquad (7.7\text{f})$$

or

$$\frac{P(t)}{1 - \frac{P(t)}{a}} = e^{kt}\cdot\left[\frac{P(0)}{1 - \frac{P(0)}{a}}\right], \qquad (7.7\text{g})$$

by taking the antilog of Equation (7.7f). Finally, we solve Equation (7.7g) for $P(t)$ to obtain

$$P(t) = \frac{a}{1 + \left(\frac{a}{P(0)} - 1\right)\cdot e^{-kt}}. \qquad (7.8)$$

Note that at $t=0$, Equation (7.8) correctly gives $P(0) = P(0)$, and at $t=\infty$ it gives $P(\infty) = a$. Equation (7.8) is often written as

$$P(t) = \frac{1}{A + Be^{-kt}}, \qquad (7.9)$$

where $A = \frac{1}{a}$ (so that $P(\infty) = a = \frac{1}{A}$), and B is a constant such that $P(0) = \frac{1}{A+B}$.

Example 7.3

Given $P(0) = 10$ million, $k = 1.25\%$, and $a = 35$ million, determine the logistic curve $P(t) = \dfrac{1}{A + Be^{-kt}}$, and estimate the population values $P(10)$ and $P(50)$.

Solution

$A = \frac{1}{a} = 2.8571 \times 10^{-8}$, and $B = \dfrac{1}{P(0)} - A = 7.1428 \times 10^{-8}$. This gives us

$$P(t) = \frac{1}{(2.8571 + 7.1428e^{-.0125t}) \times 10^{-8}}.$$

From this we find $P(10) = 10.92$ million and $P(50) = 14.97$ million. The curve is illustrated in the following figure.

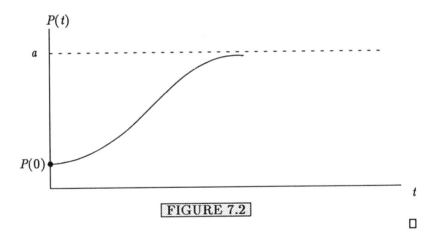

FIGURE 7.2

□

Example 7.4

Find the inflection point of the curve $P(t) = \dfrac{1}{A + Be^{-kt}}$.

Solution

From Equation (7.6) we have

$$\frac{dP(t)}{dt} = k \cdot P(t) \cdot \left[1 - \frac{P(t)}{a}\right] = k \cdot P(t) - kA \cdot \left[P(t)\right]^2,$$

so the second derivative is

$$\frac{d^2 P(t)}{dt^2} = k \cdot P'(t) - 2kA \cdot P(t) \cdot P'(t) = k \cdot P'(t) \cdot \left[1 - 2A \cdot P(t)\right].$$

At the point of inflection $\dfrac{d^2 P(t)}{dt^2} = 0$, so $k \cdot P'(t) \cdot \left[1 - 2A \cdot P(t)\right] = 0$,

which gives $P(t) = \dfrac{1}{2A}$ as the ordinate at the point of inflection.

The abscissa is then the value of t such that $\dfrac{1}{2A} = \dfrac{1}{A + Be^{-kt}}$, or

$A + Be^{-kt} = 2A$. This equation solves for $t = \dfrac{-\ln(\frac{A}{B})}{k}$. □

Another presentation of the logistic model assumes that there are census counts C_1, C_2, C_3 at equidistant times t_1, t_2, t_3, so that $(t_2 - t_1) = (t_3 - t_2)$. The logistic curve that reproduces these three points will have a population ceiling, a, given by

$$a = \frac{\dfrac{1}{C_1} + \dfrac{1}{C_3} - \dfrac{2}{C_2}}{\dfrac{1}{C_1 C_3} - \dfrac{1}{C_2^2}}, \tag{7.10}$$

provided the numerator and denominator are both positive.

Example 7.5
The following population values are given for the United States:

$$P(60) = 179,300,000 \qquad P(70) = 203,200,000 \qquad P(80) = 226,500,000$$

Estimate the ultimate size of the population using a logistic curve that reproduces the three given data points.

Solution

Using Equation (7.10) we find $a = \dfrac{\dfrac{1}{C_1} + \dfrac{1}{C_3} - \dfrac{2}{C_2}}{\dfrac{1}{C_1 C_3} - \dfrac{1}{C_2^2}} = 369,900,000.$ □

Example 7.6
Given the values $P(60) = 179.3$ million, $P(70) = 203.2$ million, and $a = 369.9$ million, find the value of $P(80)$ in the logistic model

$$P(t) = \frac{1}{A + Be^{-kt}}.$$

[Solution]

(Note first that this is really Example 7.5 in reverse. We expect the answer to be 226.5 million.)

$A = \frac{1}{a} = 2.7034 \times 10^{-9}$, and $B = \frac{1}{P(0)} - A = 2.8738 \times 10^{-9}$. Then

$$P(70) = P(10) = \frac{1}{(2.7034 + 2.8738e^{-10k}) \times 10^{-9}} = .2032 \times 10^9,$$

leading to $e^{-10k} = .77175$, and thus to $e^{-20k} = .59560$. Finally we have

$$P(80) = P(20) = \frac{1}{(2.7034 + 2.8738e^{-20k}) \times 10^{-9}} = 226.5 \text{ million},$$

as expected.   □

7.3 POPULATION PROJECTIONS: THE COMPONENT METHOD

Chapter 1 presented the formula $P(t) = P(0) + B - D + I - E$, where $P(0)$ is the population at time $t = 0$, B is the births, D is the deaths, I is the immigration, and E is the emigration for the interval from time 0 to time t. This component approach to population projection is applied by demographers using a methodology called the Leslie matrix.

Assume we have a population count on July 1, 1990 and wish to estimate the July 1, 1995 population. In particular, we have the population split by age and sex and presented in quinquennial age intervals. That is, we have data by sex of the form $_5C_0^{1990}$, $_5C_5^{1990}$, $\cdots$, $_5C_{95}^{1990}$, and so on. Note that $_5C_0$ includes all ages up to, but not including, age 5, and similarly for the other population counts.

The first stage in estimating the 1995 population is to "age" this closed group to allow for five years of survivorship. If we model the survivorship distribution by using an appropriate recent sex-specific life table, then we have $_5C_5^{1995} = {}_5C_0^{1990} \cdot \frac{_5L_5}{_5L_0}$, $_5C_{10}^{1995} = {}_5C_5^{1990} \cdot \frac{_5L_{10}}{_5L_5}$, and so on.

Thus, ignoring migration, we now have estimates for the population of each sex aged 5 and over in 1995. All that is missing is the age group 0-4.

To estimate $_5C_0^{1995}$ for the female population, we first estimate all female live births in the five-year interval and then account for their survivorship. Assume that only females aged 10 to 45 have babies, and that a recent set of age-and-sex-specific female fertility rates (denoted $_5f_{10}^f$, $_5f_{15}^f$, and so on) can be used to estimate the female births for the next five years.

Consider, for example, the female group $_5C_{25}^{1990}$. How many units will it contribute to the female group $_5C_0^{1995}$? The product $_5C_{25}^{1990} \cdot _5f_{25}^f$ is not correct for several reasons. First, over the 5-year period 1990-95, the age group $_5C_{25}^{1990}$ will experience both $_5f_{25}^f$ fertility and $_5f_{30}^f$ fertility (for those who survive past age 30). Assuming the experience is uniformly distributed, an estimate of the number of female live births is $_5C_{25}^{1990}\left(\frac{1}{2}\cdot {}_5f_{25}^f + \frac{1}{2}\cdot\frac{{}_5L_{30}}{{}_5L_{25}}\cdot {}_5f_{30}^f\right)$ [3] each year. The number of births over the 5-year period is then found by multiplying by 5.

To model the survivorship probability for the newborn females who survive to 1995 requires multiplication by $\frac{{}_5L_0}{5\cdot\ell_0}$, using the appropriate female life table. Thus the contribution of the group $_5C_{25}^{1990}$ is given by

$$5\cdot {}_5C_{25}^{1990}\cdot\frac{{}_5L_0}{5\cdot\ell_0}\left(\frac{1}{2}\cdot {}_5f_{25}^f + \frac{1}{2}\cdot\frac{{}_5L_{30}}{{}_5L_{25}}\cdot {}_5f_{30}^f\right)$$

$$= {}_5C_{25}^{1990}\cdot\frac{{}_5L_0}{\ell_0}\left(\frac{1}{2}\cdot {}_5f_{25}^f + \frac{1}{2}\cdot\frac{{}_5L_{30}}{{}_5L_{25}}\cdot {}_5f_{30}^f\right).$$

A similar expression exists for the other age groups. For example the female group $_5C_5^{1990}$ would contribute

---

[3]The mortality functions $_5L_x$ are understood to be taken from an appropriate female life table.

$$_5C_5^{1990} \cdot \frac{_5L_0}{\ell_0} \left(0 + \frac{1}{2} \cdot \frac{_5L_{10}}{_5L_5} \cdot {_5f_{10}^f}\right),$$

where the zero reminds us that $_5f_5^f = 0$.

The combination of survivorship factors and fertility-with-survivorship factors leads to the female sex-specific square matrix

$$\mathbf{M} = \begin{bmatrix} 0 & \frac{_5L_0}{\ell_0}\left(0+\frac{1}{2}\cdot\frac{_5L_{10}}{_5L_5}\cdot{_5f_{10}^f}\right) & \frac{_5L_0}{\ell_0}\left(\frac{1}{2}\cdot{_5f_{10}^f}+\frac{1}{2}\cdot\frac{_5L_{15}}{_5L_{10}}\cdot{_5f_{15}^f}\right) & \cdots \\ \frac{_5L_5}{_5L_0} & 0 & 0 & \cdots \\ 0 & \frac{_5L_{10}}{_5L_5} & 0 & \cdots \\ 0 & 0 & \frac{_5L_{15}}{_5L_{10}} & \cdots \\ \vdots & \vdots & \vdots & \vdots \end{bmatrix},$$

$$(7.11)$$

which is called a *Leslie matrix*. It is widely used by botanists, zoologists, and demographers to project the growth of plant, animal, and human populations.

All elements in the first row of a Leslie matrix become zero at the upper age of fertility, where $_5f_x^f = 0$ for all subsequent values of x. The subdiagonal elements become zero at the upper limit of the life table where $_5L_x = 0$ for all subsequent x. This determines the dimension of the matrix.

Example 7.7

Determine the female Leslie matrix to be used for a five-year projection of the Canadian female population of 1986, using the 1985-87 Canadian Life Tables with radix $\ell_0 = 100,000$. The following values are given.

Age x (1)	Number of Females $_5C_x^{1986}$ (2)	Number of Female Babies (3)	$_5f_x^f$ (3)/(2) (4)	$_5L_x$ (5)	$\dfrac{_5L_{x+5}}{_5L_x}$ (6)
0	882,415	0	0	496,315	.99854
5	874,870	0	0	495,590	.99921
10	870,050	101	.000116	495,197	.99853
15	939,600	10,362	.011028	494,471	.99794
20	1,121,895	45,412	.040477	493,453	.99791
25	1,176,520	70,021	.059515	492,420	.99749
30	1,101,880	39,844	.036160	491,182	.99657
35	1,015,120	10,812	.010650	489,497	.99456
40	803,785	1,225	.001524	486,835	.99083
45	655,915	44	.000067	482,369	.99501

Solution

Substituting these values into Equation (7.11) produces the following Leslie matrix.

$$
\begin{bmatrix}
0 & .00029 & .02762 & .12833 & .24783 & .23720 & .11607 & .03019 & .00395 & .00017 & 0 & \cdots \\
.99854 & 0 & 0 & 0 & 0 & 0 & 0 & 0 & 0 & 0 & 0 & \cdots \\
0 & .99921 & 0 & 0 & 0 & 0 & 0 & 0 & 0 & 0 & 0 & \cdots \\
0 & 0 & .99853 & 0 & 0 & 0 & 0 & 0 & 0 & 0 & 0 & \cdots \\
0 & 0 & 0 & .99794 & 0 & 0 & 0 & 0 & 0 & 0 & 0 & \cdots \\
0 & 0 & 0 & 0 & .99791 & 0 & 0 & 0 & 0 & 0 & 0 & \cdots \\
0 & 0 & 0 & 0 & 0 & .99749 & 0 & 0 & 0 & 0 & 0 & \cdots \\
0 & 0 & 0 & 0 & 0 & 0 & .99657 & 0 & 0 & 0 & 0 & \cdots \\
0 & 0 & 0 & 0 & 0 & 0 & 0 & .99456 & 0 & 0 & 0 & \cdots \\
0 & 0 & 0 & 0 & 0 & 0 & 0 & 0 & .99083 & 0 & 0 & \cdots \\
0 & 0 & 0 & 0 & 0 & 0 & 0 & 0 & 0 & .99501 & 0 & \cdots \\
0 & 0 & 0 & 0 & 0 & 0 & 0 & 0 & 0 & 0 & .97655 & \cdots \\
\vdots & \vdots & \vdots & \vdots & \vdots & \vdots & \vdots & \vdots & \vdots & \vdots & \vdots &
\end{bmatrix}
$$

The missing subdiagonal entries are $\dfrac{_5L_{60}}{_5L_{55}} = .96394, \ldots, \dfrac{_5L_{100}}{_5L_{95}} = .03639$, and $\dfrac{_5L_{105}}{_5L_{100}} = 0$, since $_5L_{100}$ is the last value of $_5L_x$ available from the life table. Thus the dimension of this Leslie matrix is 21×21. $\square$

When the matrix developed in Example 7.7 is multiplied by the 21-element vector of females given by $_5C_0^{1986}, _5C_5^{1986}, \cdots$, the vector containing the values of $_5C_0^{1991}$, $_5C_5^{1991}$, $\cdots$ is produced. This closed group population projection from 1986 to 1991 ignores migration. We could then adjust the figures to reflect the impact of five years of migration with the accuracy deemed appropriate.

The Leslie matrix could then be adjusted to reflect expected future fertility and mortality, and the process applied again to project the population another five years.

If migration is ignored and the fertility rates and mortality patterns are assumed to hold constant into the future, we can achieve an i-stage projection simply by multiplying the initial population vector by the matrix $\mathbf{M}^i$, which is the Leslie matrix multiplied by itself i times. This would project the population forward $n \cdot i$ years, where n is the size of the age groups (5 in the above example).

From the Sharpe-Lotka theorem (see Section 6.1) if we keep the Leslie matrix constant, and project far enough out, the population will become asymptotically stable. In a stable population, each age group will grow at the same rate, which is the intrinsic rate of increase r_i, and will be a constant proportion of the total population.

The projection of a population that has reached stability does not alter the relative age proportions in that population, but simply increases (or decreases) all age groups in the same ratio, λ. (See Example 7.10.) Then we have

$$\mathbf{M}\,\mathbf{K} \;=\; \lambda\,\mathbf{K}, \qquad\qquad (7.12a)$$

where $\mathbf{K}$ is the stable population vector and $\mathbf{M}$ is the Leslie matrix for this stable population. This is equivalent to

$$(\mathbf{M} - \lambda\,\mathbf{I})\,\mathbf{K} \;=\; 0, \qquad\qquad (7.12b)$$

where $\mathbf{I}$ is the identity matrix of suitable order and 0 is a vector of zeros. If the elements of $\mathbf{K}$ are not to be all zero, the matrix $\mathbf{M} - \lambda\mathbf{I}$ must be singular, so that its determinant must be zero.

This leads to the characteristic equation $\det|\mathbf{M} - \lambda\mathbf{I}| = 0$, which is a polynomial equation in λ. Its roots are values of λ called *eigenvalues*. Note that the positive eigenvalue of $\mathbf{M}$ is $\lambda = e^{n r_i}$, where n is the size of the age groups in the Leslie matrix and r_i is the intrinsic rate of increase in the stable population. That $\lambda = e^{n r_i}$ is an expected result, since we have defined λ to be the growth factor for the population over one cycle, which is n years. It was well established in Chapter 6 that this growth factor is given by e^{nr_i}.

All of the discussion so far in this section has addressed the projection of a female population vector using a Leslie matrix containing sex-specific female fertility rates and survivorship factors. It would be a mathematically identical operation to project a male population vector using a Leslie matrix containing male survivorship factors and male fertility rates $_5f_x^m$.

As pointed out in Chapter 2, however, male fertility rates are generally not available. In light of this, the male live births needed for the first row of the Leslie matrix are generally estimated from total live births by using a known sex-ratio of male to female live births. Of course the necessary male survivorship factors of $\frac{_5L_0}{5 \cdot \ell_0}$ and $\frac{_5L_{x+5}}{_5L_x}$ are readily available, so the male Leslie matrix can be completed.

| Example 7.8 |

Show that the negative of the sum of the coefficients from the second term to the last term (the constant term) of the characteristic polynomial of the Leslie matrix, **M**, is the net reproduction rate (*NRR*).

| Solution |

Let **M** denote the $n \times n$ matrix

$$
\begin{bmatrix}
a_1 & a_2 & a_3 & \cdots & a_{n-1} & a_n \\
b_1 & 0 & 0 & \cdots & 0 & 0 \\
0 & b_2 & 0 & \cdots & 0 & 0 \\
\vdots & \vdots & \vdots & \cdots & \vdots & \vdots \\
0 & 0 & 0 & \cdots & b_{n-1} & 0
\end{bmatrix}.
$$

The characteristic polynomial of **M** is given by

$$
\det|M - \lambda I| = (-1)^n \Big[\lambda^n - a_1 \lambda^{n-1} - b_1 a_2 \lambda^{n-2} - b_1 b_2 a_3 \lambda^{n-3}
$$

$$
- b_1 b_2 b_3 a_4 \lambda^{n-4} - \cdots - b_1 b_2 b_3 \cdots b_{n-2} a_{n-1} \lambda - b_1 b_2 b_3 \cdots b_{n-1} a_n \Big].
$$

$$(7.13)$$

Now let **M** be the $n \times n$ Leslie matrix defined by Equation (7.11). Then we have

$$a_1 = 0,$$

$$b_1 a_2 = \frac{{}_5 L_5}{{}_5 L_0}\left[\frac{{}_5 L_0}{\ell_0}\left(0 + \frac{1}{2} \cdot \frac{{}_5 L_{10}}{{}_5 L_5} \cdot {}_5 f_{10}'\right)\right] = \frac{1}{2} \cdot \frac{{}_5 L_{10}}{\ell_0} \cdot {}_5 f_{10}',$$

$$b_1 b_2 a_3 = \frac{{}_5 L_5}{{}_5 L_0} \cdot \frac{{}_5 L_{10}}{{}_5 L_5}\left[\frac{{}_5 L_0}{\ell_0}\left(\frac{1}{2} \cdot {}_5 f_{10}' + \frac{1}{2} \cdot \frac{{}_5 L_{15}}{{}_5 L_{10}} \cdot {}_5 f_{15}'\right)\right]$$

$$= \frac{1}{2} \cdot \frac{{}_5 L_{10}}{\ell_0} \cdot {}_5 f_{10}' + \frac{1}{2} \cdot \frac{{}_5 L_{15}}{\ell_0} \cdot {}_5 f_{15}',$$

and so on.

The total of all the coefficients, excluding the λ^n term, will be the net reproduction rate, NRR, over the period of projection. The only nonzero entries are for ages $\alpha - 5$ to β, where (α, β) is the range of fecundity.   □

Example 7.9

Using the theory of Example 7.8 and the Leslie matrix of Example 7.7, find the net reproduction rate over the period 1986 to 1991 for Canadian females.

Solution

From the matrix of Example 7.7, we find $a_1 = 0$, $b_1 a_2 = .00028735$, $b_1 b_2 a_3 = .00027557$, $b_1 b_2 b_3 a_4 = .12716018$, and so on. There are eight nonzero entries, the last being $b_1 b_2 \cdots b_8 a_9 = .00388687$. The total of these coefficients is $.7854295$. (Note that this value of NRR, which is measured over the period 1986 to 1991, differs from the value of $.785410$ produced in Table 2.4, which was the value for 1986 alone.)   □

Example 7.10

Using the following Leslie projection matrix for U.S. females, in age groups 0-15, 15-30 and 30-45, project an arbitrary population forward 480 years (32 cycles). Show that the population has reached asymptotic stability, and determine the intrinsic rate of increase for that stable population.

$$\mathbf{M} = \begin{bmatrix} .4271 & .8498 & .1273 \\ .9924 & 0 & 0 \\ 0 & .9826 & 0 \end{bmatrix}$$

Solution

We choose an arbitrary population vector as a starting population. (The reader is encouraged to try several possible starting population vectors to test the validity of the Sharpe-Lotka theorem.) For illustration we use the vector $\begin{bmatrix} 10 \\ 10 \\ 10 \end{bmatrix}$. We project this population forward 480 years using the matrix

$$\mathbf{M}^{32} = \begin{bmatrix} 255.11868 & 201.09127 & 26.85484 \\ 209.35403 & 165.01837 & 22.03747 \\ 170.10279 & 134.07950 & 17.90572 \end{bmatrix}.$$

The population after 480 years is

$$\mathbf{M}^{32} \times \begin{bmatrix} 10 \\ 10 \\ 10 \end{bmatrix} = \begin{bmatrix} 4830.6479 \\ 3964.0987 \\ 3220.8801 \end{bmatrix},$$

and the population after 495 years is

$$\mathbf{M} \times \begin{bmatrix} 4830.6479 \\ 3964.0987 \\ 3220.8801 \end{bmatrix} = \begin{bmatrix} 5841.8788 \\ 4793.9350 \\ 3895.1234 \end{bmatrix}.$$

To illustrate that the population has achieved asymptotic stability, consider the growth rates in each age group, which are

$$\frac{5841.8788}{4830.6479} = 1.2093, \frac{4793.9350}{3964.0987} = 1.2093, \text{ and } \frac{3895.1234}{3220.8801} = 1.2093.$$

Alternatively, the total population after 480 years is 12,015.6267, and the proportions in the three age groups are .40203, .33002, and .26815, respectively. After 495 years the total population is 14,530.9372, and the respective proportions are the same as they were after 480 years, as expected. To determine the intrinsic rate of increase, note that $e^{15r_i} = 1.2093$, so that $15r_i = \ln 1.2093$, which solves for $r_i = .0127$, or 1.27%. $\square$

From this example the reader might conclude that stability has, in fact, been achieved. However, if enough decimals were carried in the calculations, we would see that the population is only asymptotically stable, and true stability has not yet been achieved.

The theory presented to this point has used a constant Leslie matrix to project a given population. It has also ignored immigration. Thus we have presented a static projection method on a closed group.

In reality, the Bureau of the Census uses a far more dynamic methodology for its population projections. In fact, both the Bureau of the Census and the U.S. Social Security Administration project the population using the component method, assuming fertility, mortality, and immigration input parameters that are allowed to vary over successive projection periods. Mortality projections are usually done on a cause-sex-specific basis. Changes assumed in the mortality rates can dramatically affect the age and sex distribution results of the projected population.

Similar methods are used in Canada.

7.4 EXERCISES

7.1 Inter-Censal and Immediate Post-Censal Estimates

7-1. A country conducts a census every 5 years. Crude birth rates and death rates are constant, but births, deaths, and total population all grow by 1.5% per year, as a continuous instantaneous rate. The country continues to calculate its crude rate as $\frac{\text{Number of Births}}{\text{Population Last Census}}$. Calculate the percentage error (in absolute value) in this estimate on the day of the next census (*i.e.*, after 5 years).

7-2. The population of Miami is half Hispanic and half Caucasian as of census day in 1980. The Hispanic force of growth is $r_i = 2\%$ and the Caucasian force of growth is $r_i = .5\%$. Find the force of growth for the City of Miami between 1980 and 1990, assuming no migration and no interracial marriages.

7-3. Given the Canadian census populations $P(81) = 24,342,000$ and $P(86) = 25,354,000$, determine the difference between the geometric effective annual growth rate and the continuous instantaneous growth rate.

7-4. The City of Miami has 1 million Hispanics and 1 million whites. The Hispanic population grows at a continuous instantaneous rate of 1.5%, and the white population grows at a continuous instantaneous rate of 1%. A sociologist says that in 10 years there will be $2 \cdot e^{.125}$ million persons in Miami. Find the excess of the correct value over the estimate.

7-5. Given an average annual effective population growth rate of $\frac{1}{2}\%$, and given 6 billion people on the earth in the year 2000, when was the population of the world just two people (call them Adam and Eve)?

7-6.   A population doubles in 40 years. Find (a) the annual arith-
       metic growth rate, (b) the annual geometric growth rate,
       and (c) the continuous instantaneous growth rate.

7-7.   Many Ethiopians want to move to Canada. The population
       of Ethiopia on January 1, 1980 is 100 million and its native
       population is growing at continuous instantaneous rate
       $r_i = 2\%$. Each December 31, starting in 1980, Canada allows
       1% of Ethiopia's population to move to Canada. Once in
       Canada, Ethiopians have fewer babies and their population
       growth rate in Canada declines to $r_i = 1\%$. How many
       Ethiopians are in Canada January 1, 1990, just after the
       10th group of immigrants has arrived?

7.2   Population Projections: The Logistic Curve

7-8.   A demographer has fit a logistic curve to three data points
       to estimate the ultimate size of the population. The model
       reproduces the following three data points.

Date	Population
1989	24,000,000
1999	not legible
2009	31,000,000

       The ultimate population was determined to be 35,000,000.
       What is the missing 1999 data point?

7-9.   For the data of Exercise 7-8, assume a constant continuous
       growth factor from 1989 to 2009. What estimated 1999
       population would result from this model?

7-10. Another demographer, with the same data for 1989 as in
       Exercise 7-8, uses a logistic model with $k = .0125$. What
       1999 population would this demographer obtain using a
       logistic model with the same ultimate population?

7-11. Assume that (i) a population will reach an ultimate size of 350 million, and (ii) the population size is given by the logistic model $P(t) = \left[A + Be^{-.02t} \right]^{-1}$, $t \geq 0$. Given that $P(0) = 50$ million, determine $P(15)$.

7-12. Given the populations $P(0) = 6,000,000$, $P(20) = 16,000,000$ and $P(40) = 25,000,000$, and the model $P(t) = \dfrac{1}{A + Be^{-kt}}$, find each of the following.

(a) Ultimate size of the population.
(b) Initial rate of growth r_0.
(c) Time at which half the ultimate population is reached.

7-13. You are given (i) $P(t) = (A + Be^{-.02t})^{-1}$, and (ii) $P(\infty) = 250$ million. Determine the instantaneous relative rate of change in $P(t)$, $\dfrac{P'(t)}{P(t)}$, at the moment when $P(t) = 200$ million.

7-14. You are given that the U.S. population was 221.1 million on July 1, 1979 and 223.9 million on July 1, 1980. You are to assume that the ultimate population of the U.S. will be 800 million people.

(a) From the resulting logistic curve, what will be the population of the U.S. in the year 2000?
(b) Find the abscissa of the point of inflection for the logistic curve $P(t)$.

7-15. A population follows the logistic model $P(t) = (A + Be^{-.02t})^{-1}$. You are given (i) the point of inflection occurs at $t = 30$, and (ii) $P(30) = \dfrac{e^8}{2}$. Determine B.

7-16. A population follows a logistic model with $P(0) = 10$. Given the ratio $A/B = 3$, find the ordinate of the point of inflection for the logistic curve.

7-17. A population follows a logistic model with an ultimate population of 100 million and an abscissa at the point of inflection of $20 \ln 2$. If $k = .05$, find $P(0)$.

7-18. In Chapter 1 it was mentioned that Malthus believed there were natural checks on the maximum size of a population, such as vice, misery, and moral restraint. His theory can be expressed symbolically as

$$P_{n+1} = (1+r_a) \cdot P_n(1-P_n),$$

where P_n and P_{n+1} are proportions of the potential ultimate size of the population (so that $P_i < 1$) and r_a is some effective growth rate. For example, if a population today is only 2% of its ultimate maximum ($P_0 = .02$), but it has an explosive growth rate of $r_a = 170\%$, then it will progress as follows:

n	P_n	Comments
0	.0200	
1	.0529	Population doubles
2	.1353	Doubles again
3	.3159	And again
4	.5835	
5	.6562	Growth slows
6	.6092	Actual decline
7	.6428	
8	.6199	Heading for stability
⋮	⋮	
24	.6296	
25	.6296	Stability
⋮	⋮	
∞	.6296	

(a) Demonstrate the progression of the population if $r_a = .05$ and $P_0 = .55$.
(b) Repeat part (a) if $r_a = 2.5$ and $P_0 = .40$.

7.3 Population Projection: The Component Method

7-19. You are given the following information.

Age Last Birthday x	Population, July 1, 1986 Male	Female (Thousands)	Age-Specific Fertility Rate per 1000 Women
0-9	316	306	0
10-19	290	282	50
20-29	255	250	200
30-39	196	200	100
40-49	191	195	0

The given fertility rates are not sex-specific, but rather include births of both sexes. You are also given that the sex ratio at birth is 105 males per 100 females. Female mortality is modeled by the following life table.

x	ℓ_x	$_{10}L_x$
0	1000	9900
10	980	9720
20	960	9560
30	950	9400
40	920	9000

How many females are under age 10 on July 1, 1996?

7-20. The population of Country X is projected from July 1, 1980 to July 1, 1990. You are given that (i) the sex ratio at birth is 104 males per 100 females, (ii) the expected male population aged 0-10 inclusive on July 1, 1990 is 750,000, (iii) $_{10}L_0 = 959,000$ and $\ell_0 = 100,000$ for males, and (iv) there is no migration. Determine the expected number of births from July 1, 1980 to July 1, 1990.

7-21. You are given the following data for U.S. females in 1964.

x	Life Table $_5L_x$	Population (in thousands)	Female Births (in thousands)
0	488,970	10,136	0
5	487,312	10,006	0
10	486,502	9,065	4
15	485,484	8,045	286
20	483,940	6,546	703
25	482,030	5,614	492
30	479,486	5,632	286
35	475,789	6,193	151
40	470,394	6,345	43
45	462,418	5,796	2

(a) Ignoring migration, estimate the female population aged 0 to 15 in 1969, given $\ell_0 = 100,000$ in the associated life table.

(b) Find the net reproduction rate.

(c) Estimate the fifth entry in the first row of the Leslie matrix based on quinquennially grouped ages.

7-22. Given the following information for a certain species of commercially raised fish (female data only), calculate the total female fish population one year hence, assuming a uniform distribution of events and $\dfrac{L_0}{\ell_0} = .80$.

Age x	Current Female Population at Age x	Survival to Next Age L_{x+1}/L_x	Female Fertility Rates f_x^f
0	8000	.70	0.00
1	4500	.80	1.50
2	2000	.50	0.90
3	1100	.00	0.00

7-23. The projection matrix for a population aged 0-90 in 30-year

age groupings is $\mathbf{M} = \begin{bmatrix} .4271 & .8498 & .1273 \\ .9924 & 0 & 0 \\ 0 & .9826 & 0 \end{bmatrix}$. In 1990 the

population structure is given by the following table.

Age	Population
0-30	500
30-60	350
60-90	150

Compute the average annual rate of increase, compounded continuously, for the period 1990-2050.

7-24. You are given the Leslie matrix $\mathbf{M} = \begin{bmatrix} 0 & .1 & .2 \\ .9 & 0 & 0 \\ 0 & .8 & 0 \end{bmatrix}$ for age

groups [0-15), [15-30), and [30-45). Presently there are 10, 20, and 30 people in those age groups, respectively. How many people will be in the age group [0-15) 30 years later?

7-25. You are given the projection matrix for 15-year age groups

for females $\mathbf{M} = \begin{bmatrix} .3476 & .8917 & .1577 \\ .9952 & 0 & 0 \\ 0 & .9909 & 0 \end{bmatrix}$.

By changing the fertility rates by a constant factor, change the matrix $\mathbf{M}$ to represent a population with a rate of increase of zero. Find the sum of the elements in the second column.

7-26. The U.S. female projection matrix for ages 0-45 in 15-year

age groups with 1965 data is $\mathbf{M} = \begin{bmatrix} .4271 & .8498 & .1273 \\ .9924 & 0 & 0 \\ 0 & .9826 & 0 \end{bmatrix}$.

You are also given

$$\mathbf{M}^{32} = \begin{bmatrix} 255.11868 & 201.09127 & 26.85484 \\ 209.35403 & 165.01837 & 22.03747 \\ 170.10279 & 134.07950 & 17.90572 \end{bmatrix}.$$

(a) Using a starting population different from that used in Example 7.10, find the intrinsic rate of growth that underlies the ultimate stable rate of population growth.
(b) What is the net reproduction rate?
(c) What is the length of a generation?
(d) What would be the entry m_{11} in matrix $\mathbf{M}$ if we reduce the rate of increase to zero, without changing the force of mortality?

7-27. Let $\mathbf{M}$ denote a 3×3 projection matrix with characteristic equation $\lambda^3 - .42\lambda^2 - .84\lambda - .12 = 0$. Determine the entry in the third column and third row of $\mathbf{M}^3$.

7-28. For a population with terminal age $\omega = 90$, you are projecting the number of survivors in terms of five-year age groups. The life table of the population is assumed to follow a linear survivorship model, so that $_5L_x$ is proportional to $(87.5 - x)$ for $0 \le x \le 85$. Let $\mathbf{M}$ denote the 18×18 Leslie matrix. Determine the entry in the 16th row and the 7th column of the matrix $\mathbf{M}^9$.

7-29. $\mathbf{M}$ is a projection matrix in 15-year age groups for a female population aged 0-45. The element in the first row and first column of the matrix $\mathbf{M}^{79}$ is 1.5 times the corresponding element in the matrix $\mathbf{M}^{77}$. Calculate an estimate for r_i, the continuous instantaneous rate of increase.

7-30. You are given the following information about a female population.

    (i)   No one reaches age 100.
    (ii) The childbearing period runs from age 15 to age 50.
    (iii) The population is grouped into 10 equal intervals
        [0-10), [10-20), $\cdots$, [90-100).
    (iv) The population is projected 10 years forward using the 10×10 matrix **M**.

Determine how many elements of **M** are zero.

7-31. Use each of the following matrices to project the given population nine iterations forward. Graph the results and comment on your findings. The population vector at time 0 is $\begin{bmatrix} 1000 \\ 10 \\ 10 \end{bmatrix}$.

(a) $\begin{bmatrix} 0 & 0 & 5 \\ .7 & 0 & 0 \\ 0 & .5 & 0 \end{bmatrix}$
  (b) $\begin{bmatrix} 0 & 1 & 4 \\ .7 & 0 & 0 \\ 0 & .5 & 0 \end{bmatrix}$
  (c) $\begin{bmatrix} 0 & .1 & 4 \\ .7 & 0 & 0 \\ 0 & .5 & 0 \end{bmatrix}$

7-32. For the females of an animal species, you are given the projection matrix $\begin{bmatrix} .4 & .2 \\ .5 & 0 \end{bmatrix}$ for ages 0-10 in 5-year age groups. To reflect a change in fertility, age-specific fertility rates are multiplied by a constant so that the intrinsic rate of increase for the female population is zero. Determine the modified projection matrix.

CHAPTER 8

USES OF CENSUS DATA

8.1 INTRODUCTION

Almost all corporations use census statistics in their product marketing, facilities planning, or personnel recruitment. Companies use the population characteristics to create new products for particular target groups. In the 1960's, for example, the Ford Motor Company created the Mustang primarily for what the census revealed as a large and growing group of 18 to 24-year-olds.

The same type of census information is useful when targeting advertising and promotion efforts. Pinpointing the location of the population group that is most likely to buy a product can avoid the waste of advertising dollars. For example, advertising products like tractor lawn mowers that appeal only to home owners, can be focused on cities and towns which have primarily owner-occupied dwelling units. This information is readily obtained from printed census reports. The same data can also be used to draw sales territories and set realistic sales goals.

In facilities planning, determining that there are sufficient customers within the trading area of the store is usually done with the small area population and housing data available on census computer tapes. Prospective sites for an industrial plant can readily be evaluated using data on labor force characteristics from the census.

A new use of census summary data is in affirmative action programs. It is possible to provide evidence of past discrimination at a facility by reference to area labor force statistics by race and sex. Court cases have been won on the information found in census statistics.

The allocation of revenue sharing and many other federal and state (provincial) funds depends on census data. One example is the allocation of the seats in the U.S. House of Representatives and the Canadian House of Commons. Finally, people expect information from the census and from the collection of vital statistics about their community and their nation.

8.2   A PRACTICAL EXAMPLE: FUNDING SOCIAL SECURITY

Not surprisingly, Canada and the United States have very similar approaches to retirement income security. Both countries use a three-tiered approach to the provision of economic security in retirement, sometimes called the three-legged stool. Retirement income can be provided from government-sponsored sources, employer-sponsored plans, and individual savings. Certain tax advantages are given to monies set aside to any of these three tiers, within defined limits. In particular, some contributions can be tax-deductible (all contributions within the defined limits in Canada) and, more importantly, interest-income earned on the invested assets grows tax-free until taken.

Retirement income security systems can be funded on bases that vary from pay-as-you-go to full actuarial funding. Under the pay-as-you-go basis, contributions to the scheme during the year are just enough to pay the required benefits for that year. No assets exist in the pay-as-you-go basis. If the plan sponsor were to disappear or become bankrupt, the plan would end immediately and plan participants would have no termination benefits.

Under the full actuarial funding basis, funds are set aside on the expectation that every plan participant will be able to achieve the promised retirement income benefits accrued to date. The benefits would be provided even if the plan sponsor were to disappear or become bankrupt. In essence, every plan participant has a share of the plan assets, and plan assets can grow to very significant amounts. Inherent in the contribution required by the plan sponsor are probabilities that any one plan participant may move to another employer, die, or face some other hazard that could affect the ultimate value of the required contribution.

Almost all government-sponsored retirement-income security systems in the world are run by the pay-as-you-go philosophy. There are several reasons for this. First, in the early stages of a pay-as-you-go plan, required contributions to the scheme, either earmarked contributions or taxes, can be smaller than those required on the full actuarial funding basis. They are smaller because there are virtually always far more contributors than beneficiaries. This makes the introduction of government-sponsored retirement-income security schemes easier for the politicians to sell to the electorate. Second, if government-sponsored retirement income security schemes required full actuarial funding, then huge amounts of money would accumulate and need to be invested. If these monies were invested totally in government bonds (*i.e.*, government debt instruments) then the value of these assets would depend totally on the ability of the government to tax the people. The system, in reality, would be no different than a full pay-as-you-go system. In fact, there would be the further disadvantage of supplying the government with easy debt backing, thus encouraging deficit spending. On the other hand, if the funds were to be invested in private sector assets, the impact on the economy would be immeasurable. In most countries, the value of the assets of the social security scheme thus funded would exceed the total value of all the shares listed on the country's stock markets. In other words, the government retirement income security scheme would end up "owning" the economy. The economic ramifications of this system are so great that no country has yet gone the route of full actuarial funding. Finally, because benefits are paid out virtually the same day that contributions are received, a pay-as-you-go system can easily be indexed to inflation.

In a plan using full actuarial funding, each and every plan participant has fund assets accruing on his or her behalf. Therefore, demographics have virtually no direct effect on their plans. Pay-as-you-go schemes, however, are heavily influenced by the demographic profile of the contributors and beneficiaries of the scheme. In particular, the ratio of beneficiaries to contributors is the key factor in establishing the level of contributions required in any pay-as-you-go scheme.

Example 8.1

A country with a stable population, growing at rate r, provides each citizen aged 65 and over with a dollar per year for life. The scheme is funded on a pay-as-you-go basis through annual premiums, π, paid by all persons aged 20 to 65. Find an expression for the value of π. Also, compare this Social Security scheme to a private fully-funded scheme with the same contributions and benefits.

Using the formula developed for Example 6.15, the pay-as-you-go premium is

$$
\pi = \frac{\int_{65}^{\infty} e^{-r_i x} \cdot S(x)\, dx}{\int_{20}^{65} e^{-r_i x} \cdot S(x)\, dx} = \frac{\int_{65}^{\infty} e^{-r_i x} \cdot \ell_x\, dx}{\int_{20}^{65} e^{-r_i x} \cdot \ell_x\, dx} \ .
$$

Note that there is no interest income factor since any contributions that come in are immediately paid out as benefits.

For the private scheme, the intrinsic rate of increase r_i is irrelevant since each participant is funded separately and independently. On the other hand, there is an interest income factor that must be included since contributions will earn interest until taken as benefits. While it is not the topic of this text, it can be shown that a unit asset invested at nominal rate of interest δ per annum compounded continuously, for t years will have an accumulated value of $e^{\delta t}$. If we look at the equation of value for this arrangement as of age 65, we have the following results.

Accumulated Value of Expected Contributions: $\displaystyle \pi \int_{20}^{65} \frac{e^{\delta(65-x)}\, \ell_x}{\ell_{65}}\, dx$

Present Value of Expected Benefits: $\displaystyle \int_{65}^{\infty} \frac{e^{-\delta(x-65)}\, \ell_x}{\ell_{65}}\, dx$

Thus we have

$$
\pi = \frac{\dfrac{e^{65\delta}}{\ell_{65}} \int_{65}^{\infty} e^{-\delta x}\, \ell_x\, dx}{\dfrac{e^{65\delta}}{\ell_{65}} \int_{20}^{65} e^{-\delta x}\, \ell_x\, dx} = \frac{\int_{65}^{\infty} e^{-\delta x}\, \ell_x\, dx}{\int_{20}^{65} e^{-\delta x}\, \ell_x\, dx}. \qquad \square
$$

The above example shows that the contribution rate required for a pay-as-you-go scheme can be equivalent to that for an actuarially fully-funded scheme if the rate of growth of the population is equal to the rate of interest that can be earned on invested assets from the private plan.

Figure 2.2 indicated that crude rates of natural increase in the U.S. and Canada have not exceeded 2.1 percent per year in this century. At first glance, this seems to imply that Social Security can never be "as good a deal" as a privately funded plan since interest rates today on most assets exceed 10 percent per year. However, Social Security benefits in both Canada and the United

States are indexed to the cost-of-living, with some minor exceptions. That is, they pay benefits that retain their purchasing power. If a private plan required fully indexed benefits then it can be shown that a portion of the interest earnings represented by the force of interest δ would be consumed by the cost of indexation. For example, assume that assets can earn 11% per year but the benefits should grow by 5% per year to retain their purchasing power. It can be shown that a Social Security funding formula with $r_i \approx 6\%$ (11% minus 5%) would be equivalent. Similarly, if the interest rate was 7% and inflation was 4%, then a Social Security funding formula with $r_i \approx 3\%$ would be equivalent.

Example 8.2

What would be the effect on the pension burden of a country, and the required contribution rate for its Social Security scheme, if its intrinsic rate of natural increase, $r_i > 0$, were to change?

Solution

Example 6.16 showed that $\frac{d}{dr_i}\ln(PB) = \bar{x}_1 - \bar{x}_2$, where $\bar{x}_1$ is the average age of those aged 20 to 65 and $\bar{x}_2$ is the average age of those aged 65 and over. That is, the rate of change in the pension burden is an exponential function of $\bar{x}_1 - \bar{x}_2$. Consider, for example, a country where $\bar{x}_1 = 35$ and $\bar{x}_2 = 75$, a not unlikely scenario. In this example, for every percentage point change in r_i there will be a 40% change in the pension burden in the opposite direction! This can be seen from the expression $\frac{\Delta PB}{PB} \approx (\bar{x}_1 - \bar{x}_2)\Delta r_i = -40\Delta r_i$. Hence, we can see that the funding rate of any pay-as-you-go Social Security scheme is very sensitive to the population growth rate r_i. □

Referring back to Figure 2.2, we can see a significant reduction in the crude rate of natural increase in the United States and Canada over the last quarter century. Why did this occur?

Figures 8.1 and 8.2 display the number of live births in the United States and Canada, respectively, for most of this century. Both countries experienced a dramatic demographic phenomenon after World War II often called the Postwar Baby Boom, although it is more accurate to describe the Baby Boom as those births from 1951 through 1966 (see, for example, Brown [5] and Kettle [13]).

What followed the Baby Boom in both countries was the equally dramatic Baby Bust, resulting in the Baby Boom Tidal Wave phenomenon, illustrated in Figures 8.1 and 8.2.

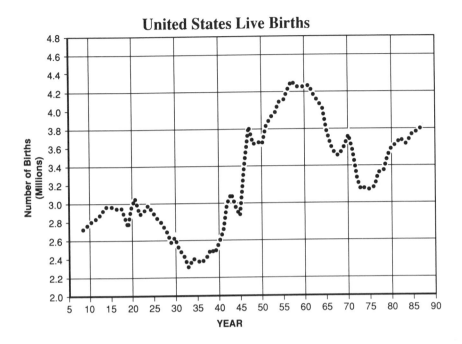

Source: [28]

FIGURE 8.1

Pertinent to the discussion of the funding of pay-as-you-go
Social Security schemes, the Baby Boom/Bust Tidal Wave creates
shifts in the pension burden, as illustrated in Tables 8.1 and 8.2 on
page 194.

Some comments are relevant. First, there is no set definition of how to calculate dependency ratios. As seen in Tables 8.1
and 8.2, the Trustees of the Old-Age, Survivors, and Disability
Insurance (OASDI) Trust Fund chose to display their dependency
ratios by using age 20 as the break point, whereas Statistics
Canada uses age 18 for the break point. Normally the denominator is used to proxy the population that could provide the
productive capacity for the economy, or the tax base. The break
point is usually a rough indicator of when young people are
expected to end their schooling and enter the labor force.

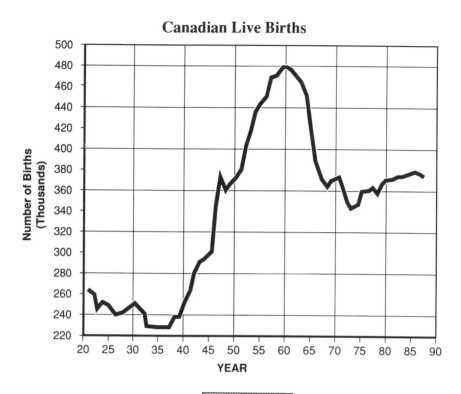

Canadian Live Births

FIGURE 8.2

Source: [25]

The Table 8.1 population projections are based on the assumptions that the total fertility rate will be 1.90 from the year 2013, immigration will total 400,000 legal immigrants and 200,000 illegal immigrants per year, and there will be continuous slow mortality improvement. The Table 8.2 projections assume a total fertility rate of 1.66 from 1996 onward, net immigration of 50,000 per year, and slowly improving mortality.

We can see that the aged dependency ratio has historically been lower in Canada, but is expected to be significantly larger than that of the United States by the end of the projection period. This difference can be explained by returning to Figures 8.1 and 8.2, which display total live births for Canada and the United States. As previously observed, Canada's Baby Boom/Bust Tidal

Wave was far more extreme than that of the United States. The
Canadian wave was higher in its peak and lower in its trough.

TABLE 8.1
U.S. DEPENDENCY RATIOS

Year	Social Security Area Population				Dependency Ratio	
	0-20	20-65	65+	Total	Aged	Total
1950	53,895	92,739	12,752	159,386	.138	.719
1960	72,989	99,842	17,250	190,081	.173	.904
1970	80,885	113,073	20,892	214,850	.185	.900
1980	74,924	134,202	26,117	235,243	.195	.753
Alternative II (Intermediate) Projection						
1990	74,289	152,569	31,965	258,823	.210	.696
2000	76,772	166,033	35,460	278,265	.214	.676
2010	74,653	179,983	39,825	294,461	.221	.636
2020	74,866	181,106	52,666	308,638	.291	.704
2030	75,094	176,223	66,486	317,803	.377	.803
2040	74,345	178,268	69,430	322,044	.389	.807

Source: [1], p. 89.

TABLE 8.2
CANADIAN DEPENDENCY RATIOS

Year	Population 65+ / Population 18-65	Population 0-18 / Population 18-65	Total Dependency
1951	.135	.608	.743
1961	.143	.728	.871
1971	.144	.634	.778
1981	.156	.452	.608
Statistics Canada Projection			
1991	.187	.390	.577
2001	.214	.356	.570
2011	.238	.311	.549
2021	.319	.312	.631
2031	.417	.324	.741

Source: [26]

This observation is confirmed by Table 8.3, which compares shifts in the aged population expected in several countries of the world over the next half century.

TABLE 8.3

PROJECTED PERCENTAGE INCREASE
IN POPULATION 65+, 1985 to 2025

Country	Percentage Increase
India	264
China	238
Hong Kong	219
Canada	135
Australia	125
Japan	121
Israel	116
U.S.	105
France	67
Italy	51
Germany	36
U.K.	23
Sweden	21

Source: [27], p. 6.

Table 8.3 shows the wide variance of the demographic shifts expected in several countries over the next half century. While India, China, and Hong Kong have the largest increase in their population aged 65 and over, they do not face any funding problems with their government-sponsored, pay-as-you-go retirement income security schemes. They have no funding problems because they really do not have benefits of any significance in place at this time. These countries are only now reaching the point of wealth where such schemes become feasible.

At the other end of the scale, France, Italy, Germany, the U.K., and Sweden do not face any serious funding problems with their well-established, government-sponsored, pay-as-you-go retirement income security schemes. They face no funding problems because the number of beneficiaries is only going to increase modestly over the next 35 years.

The countries that do face funding problems are those five countries in the middle sphere who are wealthy enough to have established government-sponsored pay-as-you-go retirement income security schemes, but at the same time, face rapidly rising numbers of beneficiaries. The drop in birth rates experienced by all of these countries, especially after the mid-1960's, only exacerbates these statistics. As seen in Table 8.1, the aged dependency ratio in the United States is expected to rise 80% between 1990 and 2030, whereas in Canada (Table 8.2), that rise is expected to be 123%.

What effect will these dramatic demographic shifts have on the funding of the respective Social Security systems?

The United States operates a single-source government-sponsored Social Security scheme called the Old-Age, Survivors, and Disability Insurance system (OASDI). Covered workers pay a payroll tax on earnings up to a specified maximum limit, and the contribution is matched by the employer. In 1989 a covered worker paid 6.06 percent on a maximum taxable earnings base of 48,000. The latter is adjusted annually based on changes in average wages. These tax contributions are deposited into a federal trust fund. All benefits and administrative expenses are paid out of that trust fund and any excess is invested in government securities. Because there is a built-in requirement that there be at least a small trust fund at any time, OASDI is said to be funded on a quasi pay-as-you-go basis.

Benefits are based on the earnings record of the worker, but proportionately larger benefits are paid to lower-income workers and proportionately smaller benefits to higher-income workers. As a rough approximation, a worker who consistently earns the average industrial wage will receive a retirement benefit at age 65 equal to 40 percent of his or her final wage. At the present time, full retirement benefits are paid at age 65 with reduced benefits being available as early as age 62 and increased benefits being paid to late retirees up to age 70. Retirement income benefits are indexed to the cost of living. OASDI also pays survivors benefits, disability benefits, spouse benefits, lump-sum death benefits, and others. Other features of the OASDI plan are beyond the scope of this text.

When the Social Security Act was enacted in 1935, age 65 was selected as the normal retirement age, the earliest age at which full retirement benefits would be paid. At the present time, the normal retirement age is still age 65. Starting in 2003, however, the normal retirement age will be gradually increased to age 66 in

2009 and age 67 in 2027. Early retirement will still be allowed at age 62, but the actuarial reduction in benefits will be greater. The higher normal retirement age is designed to improve the long-term financial solvency of OASDI in anticipation of the impact of the retirement of the Baby-Boom generation starting in 2010. It also recognizes the increase in life expectancy for all retirees.

In addition to a report of past financial transactions, the law requires that the OASDI Board of Trustees make actuarial cost projections over the next 75 years for the OASDI program. Four projections are presented. Projection I is viewed as being "optimistic," projections II-A and II-B as "intermediate," and projection III as "pessimistic." Projections II-A and II-B use identical demographic assumptions, but differ in their economic assumptions.

The assumptions regarding contributions upon which the cost projections are made are as follows.

Year	OASI	DI	Total
1989	5.53	.53	6.06
1990-99	5.60	.60	6.20
2000+	5.49	.71	6.20

Based on the annual report issued in 1989, Alternative I assumes that the total fertility rate will rise to 2.20 by 2015 and then remain at that level. It also assumes minor improvements in life expectancy. Alternative II assumes fertility will be 1.91 in the immediate future, falling slightly to 1.90 in 2010 and beyond. This alternative also assumes greater improvements in mortality. Alternatives II-A and II-B differ in their economic assumptions with Alternative II-A being slightly more optimistic than Alternative II-B. Finally, Alternative III assumes that the total fertility rate will drop to 1.60 in 2015 and then remain at that level. It also assumes the greatest improvement in mortality of the three assumptions.

The long-range 75-year estimates indicate that, under the intermediate assumptions (*i.e.*, II-A, II-B), the program will experience about three decades of positive annual balances, with continuing annual deficits thereafter. Over the full 75-year period, the intermediate II-A projections show costs exceeding revenues by an actuarial deficit of .10 percent of taxable payroll, and .70 percent of taxable payroll under assumptions II-B (see Figure 8.3).

OASDI Income Rate and Cost Rate
Based on Alternative II-B

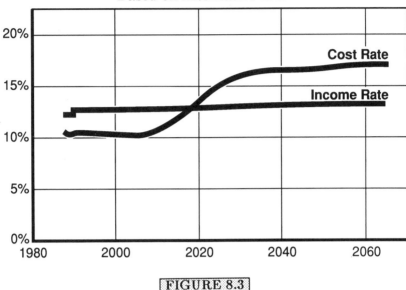

FIGURE 8.3

Source: [1], p. 8.

The trust funds are estimated to reach a level of about 5.47 times annual outgo in the year 2014 (see Figure 8.4). The actual size of the trust funds is estimated to peak at \$11.9 trillion in 2030, measured in current dollars! Measured in constant 1989 dollars (*i.e.*, deflated), the fund peaks in 2020 at \$2.8 trillion. As shown in Figure 8.4, the trust funds are projected to be exhausted in 2046 under alternative II-B because of the retirement benefits paid to the Baby Boomers.

The future funding of the OASDI scheme is not without controversy. At the moment, the OASDI surplus is included in the calculation of the federal deficit. With the rapidly rising OASDI surplus, a number of prominent members of Congress have raised concerns that this surplus is being used to mask the true federal operating deficit. Senator Daniel Moynihan has introduced legislation that would return the Social Security system to a pay-as-you-go basis. Others have suggested that the OASDI Trust Fund be removed from the calculation of the federal deficit. This matter has not yet reached a resolution.

Long-Range Contingency Fund Ratio
Based on Alternative II-B

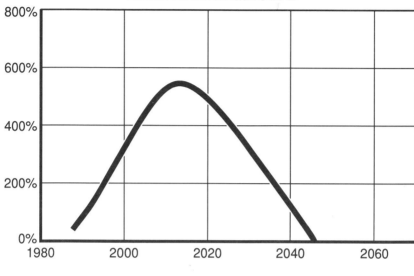

FIGURE 8.4

Source: [1], p. 9.

Canada's government-sponsored retirement income system is more complex and varied than the system used in the United States. The Canadian system has three components.

First, there is the Guaranteed Income Supplement (GIS) which is paid to Canadians 65 and over who can show need based on an income test. As of January 1, 1991, the maximum GIS benefit was $421.79 per month for a single person, and $274.73 each for a couple.

Second, there is an Old Age Security (OAS) benefit of $354.92 per month (as of January 1, 1991) which is paid to all Canadians ages 65 and over who meet a residency requirement. Partial payments are made to those who do not meet the full residency requirement. While this benefit is paid without a needs test, there is a special tax for those Canadians in receipt of the OAS who have income in excess of $51,765, which effectively taxes back the OAS benefit in full. Hence, wealthy Canadians do not receive either the GIS or the OAS. These programs are designed to guarantee a basic income net of security. These two benefits are paid from general tax revenues, and there are no contributions.

The third tier of the government-sponsored retirement income scheme is the Canada/Quebec Pension Plan (C/QPP). The differences between the Canada and the Quebec Pension Plan are very small and not relevant to this presentation. The following analysis is based solely on the Canada Pension Plan (CPP), but is indicative of the funding position of its sister Quebec Pension Plan.

The CPP has earnings-related benefits and requires contributions. In particular, workers contribute 2.50% (in 1993) of their wages up to the Average Industrial Wage ($33,400 in 1993) with these contributions being matched by the employer. There are no contributions on earnings of less than 10% of the Average Industrial Wage. In return, workers starting at age 65 can receive a retirement pension equal to 25% of their best 40 years of earnings, indexed to and capped by the Average Industrial Wage each year. A person can retire as early as age 60 with an actuarial reduction in benefits, or as late as age 70, with actuarially increased benefits. The maximum monthly benefit for someone age 65 retiring January 1, 1993 is $667.36, indexed to the cost of living. Interestingly enough, for a Canadian worker consistently earning the Average Industrial Wage, the total benefits available from all government sponsored programs will replace 40% of final earnings, exactly the same as the OASDI program in the United States.

The CPP started in 1966 with a contribution rate of 1.80% from both workers and employers (3.60% combined contribution). Because in the early years of the plan there were far more contributors than beneficiaries, and because full benefits were not paid for any retirees until 1976, a significant account balance developed. This account balance was lent to the provinces in proportion to the contributions from each province (the QPP assets are invested in real assets). The combined contribution level was left at 3.60% until 1986. In the early 1980's, it had become obvious that without an increase in the contribution rate, the provinces would have to repay some of their loans. As a result, a formula for increased contributions was put in place. The formula stipulated that the combined contribution rate would increase .20% per year for five years starting in 1987, followed by increases of .15% per year, until the year 2011, when the combined contribution rate would be 7.60%. Further amendments have recently been announced that would increase the CPP combined contribution rate to 9.10% in 2011 and 10.10% in 2016.

In evaluating the CPP plan, the actuary is trying to set a contribution rate that changes very gradually without threatening the solvency of the plan and without forcing the provinces to make significant pay-backs to the plan.

The Eleventh Statutory Actuarial Report of the Canada Pension Plan as of December 31, 1988 indicates the following statistics.

TABLE 8.4
CANADA PENSION PLAN VALUATION SUMMARY

Year	Combined Contribution Rate	Year-end Account Balance (in billions)	Ratio of Account Balance to Expenditures
1990	4.40	40.1	3.48
2000	5.95	42.7	1.88
2010	7.45	25.7	0.56
2020	11.93*	55.6	0.58
2030	13.62*	218.2	1.19
2040	13.58*	495.1	1.62
2050	13.23*	1015.0	2.01

*Although these contribution rates have not as yet been agreed to, they are the contribution rates that result in a smooth progression to an Account Balance / Expenditures Ratio of 2.00.

In this report, the actuary also produced a projection using contribution rates that increased earlier than those listed above. This was done so that the year-end account balance never falls below $40 billion, thus avoiding any provincial repayments.

Following are the demographic assumptions underlying the projections.

Mortality: 1985-87 Canada Life Tables adjusted for future
mortality improvement
Net Annual Immigration: .40% of population
Total Fertility Rates: 1.85 for Canada and 1.80 for Quebec

The report also shows projections on three different bases: (1) the assumptions used in the previous actuarial report; (2) assumptions more in line with present demographic realities; and (3) less favorable demographic assumptions. The report concludes with a section on sensitivity tests, which discusses the effects on the ultimate contribution rates of marginal changes in the demographic and economic assumptions.

The contribution rate for the CPP is projected to increase approximately threefold, from its present combined rate of 4.60% to close to 13.50%. There are two reasons for this sharp rise. First, the CPP scheme does not become fully mature until around 2010. Only then will beneficiaries have been in the plan for their full working lifetime, because the CPP only started in 1966. This is unlike the OASDI scheme which started in 1935, and therefore, has been fully mature since around 1980. The second reason for the sharp rise in projected contribution rates for the CPP is the impact of the Canadian Baby Boom/Bust Tidal Wave, which was much more dramatic both in its peak and in its trough than the similar wave in the United States.

It is through the use of evaluations such as the CPP Actuarial Report, that public-policy makers can make informed decisions as to the future funding of Social Security. In turn, these analyses depend entirely on the use of techniques introduced in this text.

8.3 CONCLUSION

This chapter has reviewed some of the practical aspects of demographics generated through an understanding of the underlying mathematics. Certainly, the actuaries whose job it is to evaluate Social Security schemes use much of the math introduced in this text on a daily basis. In dealing with politicians and policy-makers, it is particularly useful to understand some of the very easy and yet surprisingly accurate approximations introduced in the text, so as to be able to give defendable estimates on the spot without having to resort to the office computer before replying.

There is an old Chinese curse that says, "May you live in interesting times." The North American Baby Boom/Bust Tidal Wave has cursed us all to live in interesting times.

Our understanding of seemingly unrelated events is greatly enhanced by an appreciation of this dramatic demographic phenomenon. For example, the Tidal Wave has already had significant impacts on the music played daily on the radio, the number of schools, colleges and universities that were built in the 1950's and 1960's and the narrow age-range of their employees, the level of unemployment rates and the ages of highest unemployment to which government training monies should be targeted, demands for rent controls, the cost of housing, crime rates, incentives for early retirement, per capita productivity, pay for performance rather than rewards for seniority, the highly automated Japanese assembly-line, the demand for blue jeans, the age of the staff at McDonalds, and much more.

Still to come will be inevitable surprises in such areas as the decline of the housing industry, increased Gross National Savings, employer provided incentives for late retirement, increased costs for real estate in retirement states, large increases in per capita productivity, continued upward pressure on health care costs, more advertising targeted to the elderly, and much, much more.

It is the author's sincere hope that *Introduction to the Mathematics of Demography* will provide the reader with the tools to better appreciate and quantify all of these important trends. It is also the author's sincere hope that, having nibbled on the hors d'oeuvres, the reader will acquire an appetite for more knowledge in this fascinating science, and will go on to feast on much of the advanced material available on this topic. The bibliography in this text and a well-stocked university library are good places to start.

Enjoy!

8.4 EXERCISES

8.1 Introduction
8.2 A Practical Example: Funding Social Security

8-1. Consider the following data.

$_{18}P_0 = 7$ million $\qquad _{47}P_{18} = 12$ million $\qquad _{\infty}P_{65} = 6$ million

From this data, calculate the following ratios.

(a) Youth dependency ratio
(b) Aged dependency ratio
(c) Total dependency ratio

8-2. Given the data from Question 8-1, calculate the *expenditure dependency ratio*, a total dependency ratio that assumes that the government spends three times as much on supporting the elderly as it does on supporting the young.

8-3. Using the data in Table 8.1, calculate the expenditure dependency ratios for 1980, 1990, 2000, 2010, 2020, 2030, and 2040. (a) Normalize the 1980 ratio at 1.000, express the others as multiples of the normalized 1980 value, and (b) find the annual effective growth rate in the expenditure dependency ratios over the full period 1980 to 2040.

8-4. In 1990 the Canadian government announced an increase in immigration for 1991 of 150,000. Studies have shown that most immigrants are of working age. If the majority of the 1991 immigrants are aged 25 to 40, will this increased level of immigration help control the rising aged dependency ratio problem in Canada? Explain why or why not.

8-5. Assuming that the Easterlin wave theory of fertility is valid, discuss the impact it would have on the aged dependency ratios shown in Tables 8.1 and 8.2.

8-6. Assume that because of population aging, health care costs are expected to rise 70% over the next 50 years. What real effective annual growth in productivity is required to fund this growth in costs if health care costs are not going to increase as a percentage of GNP?

8-7. Consider the following information.

(i) The aged dependency ratio and youth dependency ratio were .20 and .40, respectively, at the beginning of 1985.

(ii) Since the beginning of 1985, the aged dependency ratio has increased at a rate of 2% compounded continuously.

(iii) Since the beginning of 1985, the youth dependency ratio has decreased arithmetically at an annual rate of k%.

(iv) The total dependency ratio at the beginning of 1992 is the same as it was at the beginning of 1985.

Using this information, find k.

8-8. (a) Assume that Canadian Old Age Security is paid to all Canadians aged 65 and over and funded by general tax revenues from workers aged 18 to 64. Further assume that the OAS payment (benefit) is $100k\%$ of the Average Industrial Wage, so that the retirement benefit is indexed to the Average Industrial Wage. Determine the effective *annual* growth in the tax rate needed to fund the OAS system from 1991 to 2031, assuming no change in labor force participation rates.

   (b) Now assume that the OAS benefit is indexed to the cost of living, as measured by the Consumer Price Index (CPI), rather than the Average Industrial Wage. Assume further that $\frac{1+\Delta_{AIW}}{1+\Delta_{CPI}} = 1.01$ every year, where Δ_{AIW} and Δ_{CPI} are the annual effective growth rates in wages and cost of living, respectively. Determine the effective annual growth in the tax rate needed to fund the OAS system from 1991 to 2031.

8-9. Two countries have the same life table. Country X is increasing at rate $r_i = 1\%$ and Country Y is increasing at rate $r_i = 1.25\%$. In Country X the aged dependency ratio is 10.1%, the average age of the elderly is 75, and the average age of the labor force is 35. Find the aged dependency ratio for Country Y.

8-10. The mean age of a particular population is 30 and the mean age of those aged 65 and over is 70. Given that $r_i = .005$ and that in the associated life table 10 percent of the "population" is aged 65 and over, determine the proportion of the particular population that is aged 65 and over.

APPENDIX A

DERIVATION OF EQUATION (1.3)

Let the population in a particular jurisdiction be denoted by N. If one in six households are sampled, then the sample size is $n=\frac{N}{6}$. Each household in the sample is asked if it has a particular characteristic. Let y denote the number of households in the sample that responded positively. Then $X=6y$ is a point estimate of the number of households in the jurisdiction with this characteristic. Let p denote the proportion of households in the jurisdiction with the characteristic. Then $\hat{p}=\frac{y}{n}=\frac{6y}{N}=\frac{X}{N}$ is the natural estimate of p.

We seek the estimated value of the standard error of the estimate of X. The standard error is the square root of the estimated variance of X, multiplied by the finite population adjustment factor $\frac{N-n}{N}$, which is $\frac{N-\frac{N}{6}}{N} = \frac{5}{6}$ in this case.

To find the variance of X, first define x_i to be the Bernoulli random variable for the response of the ith member in the sample, where $x_i=1$ if the member has the characteristic and $x_i=0$ if not. Then it follows that $X=6\sum_{i=1}^{n} x_i$, and

$$Var(X) = 36 \cdot Var\left(\sum_{i=1}^{n} x_i\right).$$

Since x_i is Bernoulli, then $Var(x_i) = p(1-p)$, and, since the set of x_i are mutually independent, then the variance of the sum is the sum of the variances. This leads to

$$Var(X) = 36\left(\sum_{i=1}^{n} Var(x_i)\right) = 36 \cdot np(1-p).$$

Finally, the standard error of estimate for X is given by

$$SE_X = \sqrt{\frac{5}{6} \cdot Var(X)}$$

$$= \sqrt{\frac{5}{6}(36)\left(\frac{N}{6}\right)\left(\frac{X}{N}\right)\left(1-\frac{X}{N}\right)}$$

$$= \sqrt{5X\left(1-\frac{X}{N}\right)},$$

which is Equation (1.3).

APPENDIX B

THE 1979-81 U.S. LIFE TABLES

LIFE TABLE FOR MALES

Age Interval	$_tq_x$	ℓ_x	$_td_x$	$_tL_x$	T_x	$\overset{o}{e}_x$
DAYS						
0-1	.00503	100,000	503	273	7,011,493	70.11
1-7	.00278	99,497	277	1,633	7,011,220	70.47
7-28	.00152	99,220	150	5,705	7,009,587	70.65
28-365	.00467	99,070	463	91,256	7,003,882	70.70
YEARS						
0-1	.01393	100,000	1,393	98,867	7,011,493	70.11
1-2	.00101	98,607	99	98,557	6,912,626	70.10
2-3	.00073	98,508	72	98,472	6,814,069	69.17
3-4	.00058	98,436	57	98,408	6,715,597	68.22
4-5	.00047	98,379	46	98,356	6,617,189	67.26
5-6	.00042	98,333	42	98,312	6,518,833	66.29
6-7	.00039	98,291	39	98,272	6,420,521	65.32
7-8	.00036	98,252	35	98,234	6,322,249	64.35
8-9	.00032	98,217	31	98,202	6,224,015	63.37
9-10	.00026	98,186	26	98,173	6,125,813	62.39
10-11	.00021	98,160	21	98,150	6,027,640	61.41
11-12	.00021	98,139	20	98,129	5,929,490	60.42
12-13	.00030	98,119	29	98,104	5,831,361	59.43
13-14	.00048	98,090	47	98,066	5,733,257	58.45
14-15	.00072	98,043	71	98,008	5,635,191	57.48
15-16	.00096	97,972	94	97,925	5,537,183	56.52
16-17	.00118	97,878	116	97,820	5,439,258	55.57
17-18	.00137	97,762	134	97,695	5,341,438	54.64
18-19	.00153	97,628	149	97,554	5,243,743	53.71
19-20	.00167	97,479	163	97,398	5,146,189	52.79

LIFE TABLE FOR MALES

CONTINUED

Age Interval	$_tq_x$	ℓ_x	$_td_x$	$_tL_x$	T_x	$\overset{o}{e}_x$
20-21	.00181	97,316	175	97,228	5,048,791	51.88
21-22	.00194	97,141	189	97,047	4,951,563	50.97
22-23	.00203	96,952	196	96,854	4,854,516	50.07
23-24	.00205	96,756	199	96,656	4,757,662	49.17
24-25	.00203	96,557	196	96,459	4,661,006	48.27
25-26	.00199	96,361	192	96,265	4,564,547	47.37
26-27	.00196	96,169	189	96,074	4,468,282	46.46
27-28	.00193	95,980	185	95,888	4,372,208	45.55
28-29	.00191	95,795	183	95,704	4,276,320	44.64
29-30	.00191	95,612	182	95,521	4,180,616	43.72
30-31	.00191	95,430	183	95,338	4,085,095	42.81
31-32	.00191	95,247	181	95,157	3,989,757	41.89
32-33	.00193	95,066	184	94,974	3,894,600	40.97
33-34	.00198	94,882	187	94,789	3,799,626	40.05
34-35	.00205	94,695	194	94,597	3,704,837	39.12
35-36	.00216	94,501	204	94,399	3,610,240	38.20
36-37	.00229	94,297	216	94,189	3,515,841	37.28
37-38	.00244	94,081	229	93,967	3,421,652	36.37
38-39	.00261	93,852	245	93,729	3,327,685	35.46
39-40	.00280	93,607	262	93,477	3,233,956	34.55
40-41	.00303	93,345	283	93,203	3,140,479	33.64
41-42	.00332	93,062	308	92,908	3,047,276	32.74
42-43	.00363	92,754	337	92,586	2,954,368	31.85
43-44	.00398	92,417	368	92,232	2,861,782	30.97
44-45	.00435	92,049	400	91,849	2,769,550	30.09
45-46	.00476	91,649	436	91,431	2,677,701	29.22
46-47	.00522	91,213	476	90,975	2,586,270	28.35
47-48	.00576	90,737	523	90,475	2,495,295	27.50
48-49	.00638	90,214	575	89,927	2,404,820	26.66
49-50	.00705	99,639	632	89,323	2,314,893	25.82

LIFE TABLE FOR MALES

CONTINUED

Age Interval	$_tq_x$	ℓ_x	$_td_x$	$_tL_x$	T_x	$\overset{\circ}{e}_x$
50-51	.00775	89,007	690	88,662	2,225,570	25.00
51-52	.00846	88,317	747	87,944	2,136,908	24.20
52-53	.00924	87,570	809	87,166	2,048,964	23.40
53-54	.01010	86,761	876	86,323	1,961,798	22.61
54-55	.01105	85,885	949	85,410	1,875,475	21.84
55-56	.01206	84,936	1,024	84,424	1,790,065	21.08
56-57	.01310	83,912	1,099	83,362	1,705,641	20.33
57-58	.01423	82,813	1,179	82,224	1,622,279	19.59
58-59	.01549	81,634	1,264	81,002	1,540,055	18.87
59-60	.01690	80,370	1,358	79,691	1,459,053	18.15
60-61	.01846	79,012	1,459	78,282	1,379,362	17.46
61-62	.02016	77,553	1,563	76,772	1,301,080	16.78
62-63	.02201	75,990	1,673	75,154	1,224,308	16.11
63-64	.02398	74,317	1,782	73,426	1,149,154	15.46
64-65	.02604	72,535	1,889	71,591	1,075,728	14.83
65-66	.02817	70,646	1,990	69,651	1,004,137	14.21
66-67	.03044	68,656	2,090	67,611	934,486	13.61
67-68	.03289	66,566	2,189	65,472	866,875	13.02
68-69	.03563	64,377	2,294	63,229	801,403	12.45
69-70	.03868	62,083	2,402	60,883	738,174	11.89
70-71	.04207	59,681	2,510	58,426	677,291	11.35
71-72	.04571	57,171	2,614	55,864	618,865	10.82
72-73	.04951	54,557	2,701	53,206	563,001	10.32
73-74	.05338	51,856	2,768	50,472	509,795	9.83
74-75	.05736	49,088	2,816	47,680	459,323	9.36
75-76	.06167	46,272	2,853	44,846	411,643	8.90
76-77	.06647	43,419	2,886	41,975	366,797	8.45
77-78	.07170	40,533	2,907	39,080	324,822	8.01
78-79	.07740	37,626	2,912	36,170	285,742	7.59
79-80	.08365	34,714	2,904	33,262	249,572	7.19

LIFE TABLE FOR MALES

CONTINUED

Age Interval	$_tq_x$	ℓ_x	$_td_x$	$_tL_x$	T_x	$\overset{o}{e}_x$
80-81	.09069	31,810	2,885	30,368	216,310	6.80
81-82	.09859	28,925	2,851	27,499	185,942	6.43
82-83	.10708	26,074	2,792	24,678	158,443	6.08
83-84	.11579	23,282	2,696	21,933	133,765	5.75
84-85	.12463	20,586	2,566	19,303	111,832	5.43
85-86	.13419	18,020	2,418	16,812	92,529	5.13
86-87	.14479	15,602	2,259	14,472	75,717	4.85
87-88	.15554	13,343	2,075	12,306	61,245	4.59
88-89	.16618	11,268	1,873	10,331	48,939	4.34
89-90	.17700	9,395	1,663	8,564	38,608	4.11
90-91	.18848	7,732	1,457	7,004	30,044	3.89
91-92	.20125	6,275	1,263	5,643	23,040	3.67
92-93	.21542	5,012	1,080	4,472	17,397	3.47
93-94	.23080	3,932	907	3,479	12,925	3.29
94-95	.24641	3,025	746	2,652	9,446	3.12
95-96	.26149	2,279	596	1,982	6,794	2.98
96-97	.27438	1,683	461	1,452	4,812	2.86
97-98	.28654	1,222	351	1,046	3,360	2.75
98-99	.29797	871	259	742	2,314	2.65
99-100	.30867	612	189	517	1,572	2.57
100-101	.31865	423	135	356	1,055	2.49
101-102	.32792	288	94	241	699	2.43
102-103	.33650	194	65	161	458	2.36
103-104	.34443	129	45	106	297	2.31
104-105	.35174	84	29	70	191	2.26
105-106	.35845	55	20	45	121	2.22
106-107	.36461	35	13	28	76	2.18
107-108	.37024	22	8	19	48	2.14
108-109	.37539	14	5	11	29	2.10
109-110	.38009	9	4	7	18	2.07

LIFE TABLE FOR FEMALES

Age Interval	$_t q_x$	ℓ_x	$_t d_x$	$_t L_x$	T_x	$\overset{\circ}{e}_x$
DAYS						
0-1	.00421	100,000	421	273	7,762,496	77.62
1-7	.00212	99,579	211	1,636	7,762,223	77.95
7-28	.00126	99,368	124	5,713	7,760,587	78.10
28-365	.00366	99,244	364	91,463	7,754,874	78.14
YEARS						
0-1	.01120	100,000	1,120	99,085	7,762,496	77.62
1-2	.00086	98,880	84	98,838	7,663,411	77.50
2-3	.00056	98,796	56	98,768	7,564,573	76.57
3-4	.00042	98,740	41	98,720	7,465,805	75.61
4-5	.00033	98,699	33	98,682	7,367,085	74.64
5-6	.00031	98,666	30	98,651	7,268,403	73.67
6-7	.00027	98,636	27	98,623	7,169,752	72.69
7-8	.00024	98,609	24	98,596	7,071,129	71.71
8-9	.00022	98,585	22	98,575	6,972,533	70.73
9-10	.00019	98,563	19	98,553	6,873,958	69.74
10-11	.00018	98,544	17	98,536	6,775,405	68.75
11-12	.00018	98,527	18	98,518	6,676,869	67.77
12-13	.00020	98,509	20	98,499	6,578,351	66.78
13-14	.00026	98,489	25	98,477	6,479,852	65.79
14-15	.00033	98,464	32	98,448	6,381,375	64.81
15-16	.00040	98,432	40	98,411	6,282,927	63.83
16-17	.00047	98,392	46	98,369	6,184,516	62.86
17-18	.00052	98,346	52	98,320	6,086,147	61.89
18-19	.00055	98,294	54	98,267	5,987,827	60.92
19-20	.00057	98,240	56	98,212	5,889,560	59.95
20-21	.00058	98,184	57	98,156	5,791,348	58.98
21-22	.00060	98,127	59	98,097	5,693,192	58.02
22-23	.00062	98,068	61	98,037	5,595,095	57.05
23-24	.00063	98,007	61	97,977	5,497,058	56.09
24-25	.00064	97,946	63	97,914	5,399,081	55.12

LIFE TABLE FOR FEMALES

CONTINUED

Age Interval	$_tq_x$	ℓ_x	$_td_x$	$_tL_x$	T_x	$\overset{\circ}{e}_x$
25-26	.00065	97,883	63	97,851	5,301,167	54.16
26-27	.00066	97,820	65	97,788	5,203,316	53.19
27-28	.00067	97,755	66	97,722	5,105,528	52.23
28-29	.00070	97,689	68	97,655	5,007,806	51.26
29-30	.00072	97,621	70	97,586	4,910,151	50.30
30-31	.00075	97,551	74	97,514	4,812,565	49.33
31-32	.00079	97,477	77	97,439	4,715,051	48.37
32-33	.00083	97,400	81	97,360	4,617,612	47.41
33-34	.00089	97,319	86	97,276	4,520,252	46.45
34-35	.00096	97,233	93	97,186	4,422,976	45.49
35-36	.00104	97,140	101	97,089	4,325,790	44.53
36-37	.00114	97,039	111	96,984	4,228,701	43.58
37-38	.00125	96,928	121	96,868	4,131,717	42.63
38-39	.00137	96,807	132	96,741	4,034,849	41.68
39-40	.00149	96,675	144	96,603	3,938,108	40.74
40-41	.00163	96,531	157	96,452	3,841,505	39.80
41-42	.00180	96,374	174	96,287	3,745,053	38.86
42-43	.00199	96,200	191	96,104	3,648,766	37.93
43-44	.00218	96,009	210	95,904	3,552,662	37.00
44-45	.00239	95,799	229	95,684	3,456,758	36.08
45-46	.00262	95,570	250	95,445	3,361,074	35.17
46-47	.00286	95,320	273	95,184	3,265,629	34.26
47-48	.00315	95,047	299	94,897	3,170,445	33.36
48-49	.00347	94,748	329	94,584	3,075,548	32.46
49-50	.00381	94,419	359	94,239	2,980,964	31.57
50-51	.00416	94,060	391	93,864	2,886,725	30.69
51-52	.00452	93,669	424	93,457	2,792,861	29.82
52-53	.00490	93,245	457	93,017	2,699,404	28.95
53-54	.00532	92,788	494	92,541	2,606,387	28.09
54-55	.00578	92,294	534	92,028	2,513,846	27.24

LIFE TABLE FOR FEMALES

CONTINUED

Age Interval	$_t q_x$	ℓ_x	$_t d_x$	$_t L_x$	T_x	$\overset{\circ}{e}_x$
55-56	.00627	91,760	575	91,472	2,421,818	26.39
56-57	.00678	91,185	618	90,876	2,330,346	25.56
57-58	.00733	90,567	664	90,235	2,239,470	24.73
58-59	.00796	89,903	716	89,545	2,149,235	23.91
59-60	.00867	89,187	773	88,800	2,059,690	23.09
60-61	.00947	88,414	837	87,996	1,970,890	22.29
61-62	.01035	87,577	907	87,123	1,882,894	21.50
62-63	.01129	86,670	979	86,181	1,795,771	20.72
63-64	.01226	85,691	1,050	85,166	1,709,590	19.95
64-65	.01325	84,641	1,121	84,081	1,624,424	19.19
65-66	.01427	83,520	1,192	82,923	1,540,343	18.44
66-67	.01538	82,328	1,267	81,695	1,457,420	17.70
67-68	.01664	81,061	1,349	80,387	1,375,725	16.97
68-69	.01811	79,712	1,443	78,990	1,295,338	16.25
69-70	.01980	78,269	1,549	77,495	1,216,348	15.54
70-71	.02169	76,720	1,665	75,887	1,138,853	14.84
71-72	.02375	75,055	1,782	74,164	1,062,966	14.16
72-73	.02600	73,273	1,905	72,321	988,802	13.49
73-74	.02842	71,368	2,028	70,354	916,481	12.84
74-75	.03106	69,340	2,154	68,263	846,127	12.20
75-76	.03388	67,186	2,276	66,048	777,864	11.58
76-77	.03704	64,910	2,404	63,707	711,816	10.97
77-78	.04073	62,506	2,546	61,233	648,109	10.37
78-79	.04515	59,960	2,707	58,607	586,876	9.79
79-80	.05033	57,253	2,881	55,812	528,269	9.23
80-81	.05622	54,372	3,057	52,844	472,457	8.69
81-82	.06269	51,315	3,217	49,706	419,613	8.18
82-83	.06973	48,098	3,354	46,422	369,907	7.69
83-84	.07722	44,744	3,455	43,016	323,485	7.23
84-85	.08519	41,289	3,517	39,531	280,469	6.79

LIFE TABLE FOR FEMALES

CONTINUED

Age Interval	$_tq_x$	ℓ_x	$_td_x$	$_tL_x$	T_x	$\overset{\circ}{e}_x$
85-86	.09409	37,772	3,554	35,995	240,938	6.38
86-87	.10405	34,218	3,561	32,437	204,943	5.99
87-88	.11420	30,657	3,501	28,907	172,506	5.63
88-89	.12427	27,156	3,374	25,469	143,599	5.29
89-90	.13471	23,782	3,204	22,180	118,130	4.97
90-91	.14661	20,578	3,017	19,069	95,950	4.66
91-92	.16024	17,561	2,814	16,154	76,881	4.38
92-93	.17460	14,747	2,575	13,459	60,727	4.12
93-94	.18904	12,172	2,301	11,022	47,268	3.88
94-95	.20348	9,871	2,009	8,867	36,246	3.67
95-96	.21823	7,862	1,715	7,004	27,379	3.48
96-97	.23221	6,147	1,428	5,433	20,375	3.31
97-98	.24560	4,719	1,159	4,140	14,942	3.17
98-99	.25834	3,560	919	3,101	10,802	3.03
99-100	.27040	2,641	714	2,283	7,701	2.92
100-101	.28176	1,927	543	1,655	5,418	2.81
101-102	.29242	1,384	405	1,182	3,763	2.72
102-103	.30237	979	296	831	2,581	2.64
103-104	.31163	683	213	577	1,750	2.56
104-105	.32023	470	150	394	1,173	2.50
105-106	.32817	320	105	268	779	2.44
106-107	.33550	215	72	178	511	2.38
107-108	.34224	143	49	119	333	2.33
108-109	.34843	94	33	77	214	2.28
109-110	.35411	61	22	50	137	2.24

APPENDIX C

THE 1985-87 CANADIAN LIFE TABLES

LIFE TABLE FOR THE FIRST YEAR OF LIFE (MALE)

Age Interval	ℓ_x	d_x	p_x	q_x	L_x	T_x	$\overset{\circ}{e}_x$
0 - 1 day	100,000	318	.99682	.00318	273	7,304,280	73.04
1 - 2 days	99,682	46	.99995	.00045	273	7,304,006	73.27
2 - 3 days	99,636	35	.99964	.00036	273	7,303,733	73.30
3 - 4 days	99,601	23	.99977	.00023	273	7,303,460	73.33
4 - 5 days	99,578	16	.99984	.00016	273	7,303,188	73.34
5 - 6 days	99,562	13	.99987	.00013	273	7,302,915	73.35
6 - 7 days	99,549	10	.99990	.00010	273	7,302,642	73.36
0 - 7 days	100,000	461	.99539	.00461	1911	7,304,280	73.04
7 - 14 days	99,539	48	.99952	.00048	1908	7,302,369	73.36
14 - 21 days	99,491	24	.99976	.00024	1908	7,300,461	73.38
21 - 28 days	99,467	20	.99980	.00020	1907	7,298,553	73.38
0 - 28 days	100,000	553	.99447	.00553	7634	7,304,280	73.04
1 - 2 months	99,447	68	.99931	.00069	8839	7,296,645	73.37
2 - 3 months	99,379	66	.99934	.00066	8289	7,287,806	73.33
3 - 4 months	99,313	49	.99951	.00049	8284	7,279,517	73.30
4 - 5 months	99,264	35	.99964	.00036	8281	7,271,232	73.25
5 - 6 months	99,229	22	.99978	.00022	8278	7,262,952	73.19
6 - 7 months	99,207	18	.99982	.00018	8277	7,254,673	73.13
7 - 8 months	99,189	13	.99987	.00013	8275	7,246,396	73.06
8 - 9 months	99,176	11	.99989	.00011	8274	7,238,121	72.98
9 - 10 months	99,165	6	.99994	.00006	8274	7,229,846	72.91
10 - 11 months	99,159	10	.99990	.00010	8273	7,221,573	72.83
11 - 12 months	99,149	7	.99993	.00007	8272	7,213,299	72.75

LIFE TABLE FOR THE FIRST YEAR OF LIFE
(FEMALE)

Age Interval	l_x	d_x	p_x	q_x	L_x	T_x	$\overset{o}{e}_x$
0 - 1 day	100,000	252	.99748	.00252	273	7,972,923	79.73
1 - 2 days	99,748	36	.99964	.00036	273	7,972,650	79.93
2 - 3 days	99,712	31	.99969	.00031	273	7,972,377	79.95
3 - 4 days	99,681	18	.99983	.00017	273	7,972,104	79.98
4 - 5 days	99,663	11	.99989	.00011	273	7,971,830	79.99
5 - 6 days	99,652	7	.99992	.00008	273	7,971,557	79.99
6 - 7 days	99,645	8	.99993	.00007	273	7,971,284	80.00
0 - 7 days	100,000	363	.99637	.00363	1912	7,972,923	79.73
7 - 14 days	99,637	36	.99963	.00037	1911	7,971,011	80.00
14 - 21 days	99,601	20	.99980	.00020	1910	7,969,101	80.01
21 - 28 days	99,581	16	.99984	.00016	1910	7,967,191	80.01
0 - 28 days	100,000	435	.99565	.00435	7642	7,972,923	79.73
1 - 2 months	99,565	57	.99943	.00057	8850	7,965,281	80.00
2 - 3 months	99,508	45	.99955	.00045	8301	7,956,431	79.96
3 - 4 months	99,463	36	.99963	.00037	8297	7,948,130	79.91
4 - 5 months	99,427	27	.99974	.00026	8295	7,939,833	79.86
5 - 6 months	99,400	17	.99983	.00017	8293	7,931,538	79.79
6 - 7 months	99,383	14	.99986	.00014	8292	7,923,245	79.72
7 - 8 months	99,369	11	.99989	.00011	8291	7,914,953	79.65
8 - 9 months	99,358	10	.99990	.00010	8290	7,906,663	79.58
9 - 10 months	99,348	10	.99990	.00010	8289	7,898,373	79.50
10 - 11 months	99,338	8	.99991	.00009	8288	7,890,084	79.43
11 - 12 months	99,330	8	.99992	.00008	8287	7,881,796	79.35

ADULT LIFE TABLE
(MALE)

Age	ℓ_x	d_x	p_x	q_x	L_x	T_x	$\overset{\circ}{e}_x$
0	100,000	858	.99142	.00858	99,253	7,304,280	73.04
1	99,142	66	.99933	.00067	99,105	7,205,027	72.67
2	99,076	50	.99950	.00050	99,048	7,105,922	71.72
3	99,026	40	.99959	.00041	99,008	7,006,874	70.76
4	98,986	36	.99964	.00036	98,968	6,907,866	69.79
5	98,950	30	.99970	.00030	98,935	6,808,898	68.81
6	98,920	23	.99976	.00024	98,909	6,709,963	67.83
7	98,897	18	.99982	.00018	98,888	6,611,055	66.85
8	98,879	16	.99984	.00016	98,871	6,512,167	65.86
9	98,863	16	.99984	.00016	98,855	6,413,296	64.87
10	98,847	18	.99982	.00018	98,838	6,314,441	63.88
11	98,829	20	.99979	.00021	98,819	6,215,602	62.89
12	98,809	28	.99972	.00028	98,795	6,116,783	61.91
13	98,781	39	.99961	.00039	98,762	6,017,989	60.92
14	98,742	55	.99944	.00056	98,715	5,919,227	59.95
15	98,687	73	.99926	.00074	98,651	5,820,512	58.98
16	98,614	90	.99909	.00091	98,569	5,721,861	58.02
17	98,524	103	.99895	.00105	98,473	5,623,291	57.08
18	98,421	114	.99885	.00115	98,364	5,524,819	56.13
19	98,307	121	.99876	.00124	98,246	5,426,455	55.20
20	98,186	128	.99870	.00130	98,122	5,328,208	54.27
21	98,058	133	.99865	.00135	97,991	5,230,087	53.34
22	97,925	136	.99862	.00138	97,857	5,132,095	52.41
23	97,789	135	.99861	.00138	97,722	5,034,238	51.48
24	97,654	133	.99864	.00136	97,587	4,936,517	50.55
25	97,521	129	.99868	.00132	97,457	4,838,929	49.62
26	97,392	125	.99871	.00129	97,330	4,741,472	48.68
27	97,267	123	.99873	.00127	97,205	4,644,143	47.75
28	97,144	124	.99873	.00127	97,082	4,546,937	46.81
29	97,020	125	.99872	.00128	96,958	4,449,856	45.87

ADULT LIFE TABLE
(MALE)
CONTINUED

Age	ℓ_x	d_x	p_x	q_x	L_x	T_x	$\overset{\circ}{e}_x$
30	96,895	126	.99870	.00130	96,832	4,352,898	44.92
31	96,769	129	.99867	.00133	96,705	4,256,066	43.98
32	96,640	131	.99864	.00136	96,575	4,159,361	43.04
33	96,509	134	.99861	.00139	96,442	4,062,786	42.10
34	96,375	136	.99859	.00141	96,307	3,966,344	41.16
35	96,239	140	.99855	.00145	96,169	3,870,038	40.21
36	96,099	144	.99850	.00150	96,027	3,773,868	39.27
37	95,955	151	.99842	.00158	95,879	3,677,841	38.33
38	95,804	162	.99831	.00169	95,723	3,581,962	37.39
39	95,642	174	.99818	.00182	95,555	3,486,239	36.45
40	95,468	189	.99803	.00197	95,374	3,390,684	35.52
41	95,279	204	.99785	.00215	95,177	3,295,311	34.59
42	95,075	225	.99764	.00236	94,962	3,200,134	33.66
43	94,850	245	.99741	.00259	94,727	3,105,171	32.74
44	94,605	269	.99716	.00284	94,470	3,010,444	31.82
45	94,336	294	.99688	.00312	94,189	2,915,974	30.91
46	94,042	325	.99655	.00345	93,880	2,821,785	30.01
47	93,717	359	.99616	.00384	93,538	2,727,905	29.11
48	93,358	400	.99571	.00429	93,158	2,634,367	28.22
49	92,958	444	.99522	.00478	92,736	2,541,210	27.34
50	92,514	493	.99468	.00532	92,267	2,448,474	26.47
51	92,021	546	.99406	.00594	91,748	2,356,207	25.61
52	91,475	606	.99338	.00662	91,172	2,264,459	24.75
53	90,869	670	.99262	.00738	90,534	2,173,287	23.92
54	90,199	739	.99181	.00819	89,829	2,082,753	23.09
55	89,460	813	.99092	.00909	89,054	1,992,924	22.28
56	88,647	890	.98995	.01005	88,202	1,903,870	21.48
57	87,757	975	.98889	.01111	87,269	1,815,668	20.69
58	86,782	1,062	.98777	.01223	86,251	1,728,399	19.92
59	85,720	1,148	.98660	.01340	85,146	1,642,148	19.16

ADULT LIFE TABLE
(MALE)
CONTINUED

Age	ℓ_x	d_x	p_x	q_x	L_x	T_x	$\overset{o}{e}_x$
60	84,572	1,242	.98532	.01468	83,951	1,557,002	18.41
61	83,330	1,341	.98391	.01609	82,660	1,473,051	17.68
62	81,989	1,451	.98230	.01770	81,264	1,390,391	16.96
63	80,538	1,568	.98053	.01947	79,754	1,309,127	16.25
64	78,970	1,689	.97861	.02139	78,126	1,229,373	15.57
65	77,281	1,814	.97653	.02347	76,374	1,151,247	14.90
66	75,467	1,942	.97426	.02574	74,496	1,074,873	14.24
67	73,525	2,076	.97176	.02824	72,487	1,000,377	13.61
68	71,449	2,208	.96911	.03089	70,345	927,890	12.99
69	69,241	2,333	.96630	.03370	68,075	857,546	12.38
70	66,908	2,457	.96327	.03673	65,679	789,471	11.80
71	64,451	2,582	.95994	.04006	63,160	723,791	11.23
72	61,869	2,708	.95623	.04377	60,515	660,632	10.68
73	59,161	2,828	.95219	.04781	57,747	600,117	10.14
74	56,333	2,936	.94788	.05212	54,865	542,370	9.63
75	53,397	3,033	.94321	.05679	51,880	487,505	9.13
76	50,364	3,116	.93812	.06188	48,806	435,625	8.65
77	47,248	3,187	.93255	.06745	45,654	386,819	8.19
78	44,061	3,236	.92656	.07344	42,443	341,165	7.74
79	40,825	3,258	.92019	.07981	39,196	298,722	7.32
80	37,567	3,255	.91335	.08665	35,939	259,526	6.91
81	34,312	3,228	.90593	.09407	32,698	223,587	6.52
82	31,084	3,177	.89781	.10219	29,496	190,889	6.14
83	27,907	3,096	.88906	.11094	26,359	161,394	5.78
84	24,811	2,983	.87977	.12023	23,320	135,035	5.44
85	21,828	2,841	.86982	.13018	20,407	111,715	5.12
86	18,987	2,676	.85910	.14090	17,649	91,308	4.81
87	16,311	2,487	.84751	.15249	15,068	73,659	4.52
88	13,824	2,279	.83512	.16488	12,684	58,591	4.24
89	11,545	2,055	.82199	.17801	10,517	45,907	3.98

ADULT LIFE TABLE
(MALE)
CONTINUED

Age	ℓ_x	d_x	p_x	q_x	L_x	T_x	$\overset{o}{e}_x$
90	9,490	1,822	.80803	.19197	8,579	35,389	3.73
91	7,668	1,586	.79312	.20688	6,875	26,811	3.50
92	6,082	1,356	.77716	.22284	5,404	19,936	3.28
93	4,726	1,091	.76915	.23085	4,181	14,532	3.07
94	3,635	839	.76918	.23082	3,216	10,351	2.85
95	2,796	661	.76369	.23631	2,466	7,135	2.55
96	2,135	556	.73923	.26077	1,857	4,670	2.19
97	1,579	502	.68226	.31774	1,328	2,813	1.78
98	1,077	460	.57249	.42751	847	1,485	1.38
99	617	359	.41890	.58110	437	638	1.04
100	258	193	.25198	.74802	162	201	.78
101	65	58	.10219	.89781	36	39	.60
102	7	7	.00000	.00000	3	3	.50

ADULT LIFE TABLE
(FEMALE)

Age	ℓ_x	d_x	p_x	q_x	L_x	T_x	$\overset{\circ}{e}_x$
0	100,000	678	.99322	.00678	99,415	7,972,923	75.73
1	99,322	62	.99938	.00062	99,286	7,873,508	79.27
2	99,260	41	.99959	.00041	99,235	7,774,222	78,32
3	99,219	30	.99970	.00030	99,204	7,674,987	77.35
4	99,189	25	.99974	.00026	99,175	7,575,783	76.38
5	99,164	22	.99978	.00022	99,153	7,476,608	75.40
6	99,142	18	.99982	.00018	99,133	7,377,455	74.41
7	99,124	16	.99984	.00016	99,116	7,278,323	73.43
8	99,108	14	.99986	.00014	99,101	7,179,207	72.44
9	99,094	13	.99986	.00014	99,087	7,080,106	71.45
10	99,081	15	.99986	.00014	99,073	6,981,018	70.46
11	99,065	15	.99985	.00015	99,059	6,881,945	69.47
12	99,051	17	.99982	.00018	99,043	6,782,886	68.48
13	99,034	17	.99979	.00021	99,023	6,683,844	67.49
14	99,013	27	.99973	.00027	98,999	6,584,820	66.50
15	98,986	32	.99968	.00032	98,970	6,485,821	65.52
16	58,954	37	.99962	.00038	98,935	6,386,851	64.54
17	98,917	41	.999959	.000041	98,897	6,287,915	63.57
18	98,876	42	.99958	.00042	98,855	6,189,019	62.59
19	98,934	42	.99958	.00042	98,813	6,090,164	61.62
20	98,792	41	.99958	.00042	98,772	5,991,350	50,65
21	98,751	40	.99959	.00041	98,731	5,892,579	59.67
22	98,711	40	.99959	.00041	98,691	5,793,848	58.70
23	98,671	41	.99959	.00041	98,650	5,895,157	57.72
24	98,630	40	.99959	.00041	98,610	5,596,507	56.74
25	98,590	41	.99959	.00041	98,569	5,497,897	55.77
26	98,549	42	.99958	.00042	98,528	5,399,328	54.79
27	98,507	43	.99956	.00044	98,486	5,300,800	53.81
28	98,464	45	.99954	.00046	98,442	5,202,314	52.83
29	98,419	47	.99952	.00048	98,395	5,103,872	51.86

ADULT LIFE TABLE
(FEMALE)
CONTINUED

Age	ℓ_x	d_x	p_x	q_x	L_x	T_x	$\overset{\circ}{e}_x$
30	98,372	50	.99943	.00051	98,347	5,005,477	50.88
31	98,322	54	.99946	.00054	98,295	4,907,130	49.94
32	98,268	57	.99942	.00058	98,240	4,808,835	48.91
33	98,211	60	.99939	.00061	98,181	4,710,596	47.96
34	98,151	64	.99935	.00065	98,119	4,612,414	46.99
35	98,087	67	.99931	.00069	98,053	4,514,295	46.02
36	98,020	73	.99926	.00074	97,983	4,416,242	45.05
37	97,947	80	.99919	.00081	97,907	4,318,259	44.09
38	97,867	88	.99910	.00090	97,823	4,220,352	43.12
39	97,779	98	.99900	.00100	97,730	4,122,528	42.16
40	97,681	109	.99888	.00112	97,626	4,024,798	41.20
41	97,572	123	.99875	.00125	97,510	3,927,172	40.25
42	97,449	136	.99860	.00140	97,381	3,829,661	39.30
43	97,313	151	.99845	.00155	97,238	3,732,280	38.35
44	97,262	167	.99828	.00172	97,079	3,635,042	37.41
45	96,995	184	.99810	.00190	96,903	3,537,963	36.48
44	96,811	203	.99790	.00210	96,710	3,441,060	35.54
47	96,608	224	.99768	.00232	96,496	3,344,350	34.62
48	96,384	258	.99743	.00257	96,260	3,247,854	33.70
49	96,136	272	.99717	.00283	96,000	3,151,554	32.78
50	95,864	299	.99689	.00312	95,712	3,055,594	31.87
51	95,565	327	.99657	.00343	95,403	2,959,880	30.97
52	95,238	359	.99624	.00376	95,056	2,864,478	30.08
53	94,879	389	.99589	.00411	94,681	2,769,420	29.19
54	94,590	423	.99553	.00447	94,277	2,674,735	28.31
55	94,067	458	.99513	.00487	93,838	2,580,457	27.43
56	93,609	496	.99470	.00530	93,361	2,486,619	26.56
57	93,113	539	.99421	.00579	92,843	2,393,258	25.70
58	92,574	586	.99368	.00632	92,281	2,300,414	24.85
59	91,988	634	.99311	.00689	91,671	2,208,133	24.00

ADULT LIFE TABLE
(FEMALE)
CONTINUED

Age	ℓ_x	d_x	p_x	q_x	L_x	T_x	$\overset{\circ}{e}_x$
60	91,354	686	.99249	.00751	90,011	2,116,462	23.17
61	90,668	744	.99179	.00821	90,296	2,025,450	22.34
62	89,924	809	.99101	.00899	89,519	1,935,155	21.52
63	89,115	877	.99015	.00985	88,676	1,845,635	20.71
64	88,238	950	.98924	.01076	87,763	1,756,959	19.91
65	87,288	1,026	.98824	.01176	86,775	1,669,196	19.12
66	86,262	1,111	.98712	.01288	85,706	1,582,421	19.34
67	85,151	1,206	.98583	.01417	84,548	1,496,714	17.58
68	83,945	1,306	.98444	.01556	83,292	1,412,167	16.82
69	82,639	1,408	.98297	.01703	81,935	1,328,875	16.08
70	81,231	1,516	.98133	.01867	80,476	1,246,940	15.35
71	79,715	1,638	.97945	.02055	78,892	1,166,467	14.63
72	78,077	1,777	.97725	.02275	77,189	1,087,572	13.93
73	76,300	1,924	.97478	.02522	75,338	1,010,383	13.24
74	74,376	2,074	.97211	.02789	73,339	935,045	12.57
75	72,302	2,232	.96913	.03087	71,186	861,705	11.92
72	70,070	2,358	.96577	.03423	68,871	790,519	11.28
77	67,672	2,576	.96193	.03807	66,384	721,649	10.66
78	65,096	2,791	.95774	.04226	63,720	655,265	10.07
79	62,345	2,916	.95324	.04676	60,887	591,549	9.49
80	59,429	3,074	.94827	.05173	57,892	530,658	8.93
81	56,355	3,232	.94265	.05735	54,739	472,766	8.39
82	53,123	3,388	.93623	.06377	51,429	418,027	7.87
83	49,735	3,526	.92910	.07090	47,972	366,598	7.37
84	46,209	3,633	.92139	.07861	44,393	318,627	6.90
85	42,576	3,707	.91292	.08708	40,723	274,234	6.44
86	38,869	3,750	.90353	.09647	36,994	233,512	6.01
87	35,119	3,756	.89304	.10696	33,241	196,518	5.60
88	31,363	3,715	.88157	.11844	29,506	163,277	5.21
89	27,648	3,615	.86923	.13077	25,841	133,771	4.84

ADULT LIFE TABLE
(FEMALE)
CONTINUED

Age	ℓ_x	d_x	p_x	q_x	L_x	T_x	$\overset{o}{e}_x$
90	24,033	3,464	.85585	.14415	22,301	107,930	4.49
91	20,569	3,265	.84126	.15874	18,936	85,630	4.16
92	17,304	3,023	.82530	.17470	15,792	66,694	3.85
93	14,281	2,607	.81747	.18253	12,977	50,901	3.56
94	11,671	2,126	.81789	.18211	10,611	37,924	3.25
95	9,548	1,792	.81229	.18771	8,652	27,313	2.86
96	7,756	1,657	.78639	.21361	6,927	18,661	2.41
97	6,099	1,672	.72591	.27409	5,263	11,734	1.92
98	4,427	1,730	.60921	.39079	3,562	6,471	1.46
99	2,697	1,495	.44581	.55419	1,950	2,909	1.08
100	1,202	880	.26817	.73183	762	959	.80
101	322	287	.10875	.89125	179	196	.61
102	35	35	.00000	1.00000	18	18	.50

APPENDIX D

FURTHER DISCUSSION OF STABLE POPULATION THEORY

D.1 SOLVING FOR r

Define $F_x(t)\,dx$ to be the number of females at time t whose ages are between x and $x+dx$, and define $B(t)\,dt$ to be the number of female births during the time interval t to $t+dt$. Assume that $t > x$. From these definitions it follows that

$$F_x(t)\,dx \ = \ B(t-x)\cdot S(x)\,dx. \tag{D.1}$$

The number of female births in the infinitesimal time interval dt from the $F_x(t)\,dx$ females whose ages are between x and $x+dx$ is denoted by $F_x(t)\,dx \cdot \phi_x^f\,dt$. Then it follows that

$$B(t) \ = \ \int_0^\infty F_x(t)\cdot \phi_x^f\,dx$$

$$= \ \int_0^\infty B(t-x)\cdot S(x)\cdot \phi_x^f\,dx \tag{D.2}$$

We follow the solution given by Rhodes (see Pollard [22]). We assume that reproduction takes place over only the female life span between ages α and β, and further assume that $B(t)$ is of the form

$$B(t) \ = \ Ae^{rt}. \tag{D.3}$$

When this is substituted into Equation (D.2) we obtain

$$Ae^{rt} \ = \ Ae^{rt}\int_\alpha^\beta e^{-rx}\cdot S(x)\cdot \phi_x^f\;dx. \tag{D.4}$$

Then r is the solution of the integral equation

$$\int_\alpha^\beta e^{-rx} \cdot S(x) \cdot \phi_x^f \, dx = 1. \tag{D.5}$$

Note that Equation (D.5) is the same as Equation (6.9), where r is used in place of r_i for later notational convenience.

| THEOREM | Equation (D.5) has exactly one real solution $r=r_0$. Any complex roots $\{r_j\}$ occur in complex conjugate pairs, and $r_0 > $ Real (r_j).

| PROOF |

(i)   To prove that there is only one real root r, we let $\Psi(r)$ denote the left side of Equation (D.5), so that

$$\Psi'(r) = \int_\alpha^\beta - xe^{-rx} \cdot S(x) \cdot \phi_x^f \, dx. \tag{D.6}$$

It should be clear that $\Psi(r) \to \infty$ as $r \to -\infty$, and $\Psi(r) \to 0$ as $r \to \infty$. But $\Psi(r)$ is a continuous function of r, so at least one real solution for Equation (D.5) exists.

Furthermore, the functions x, e^{-rx}, $S(x)$, and ϕ_x^f are all non-negative over the range of integration in Equation (D.6), and they are all simultaneously positive over part of the range of integration, so $\Psi'(r)$ is negative for all real r. Then it follows that $\Psi(r)$ is monotone strictly decreasing, and hence there is only one real solution $r=r_0$ to the equation $\Psi(r)=1$.

(ii)   Now we consider the complex roots, and assume that $u+iv$ is one such root. Equation (D.5) becomes

$$\int_\alpha^\beta e^{-ux} \{cos(-vx) + i \cdot sin(-vx)\} \cdot S(x) \cdot \phi_x^f \, dx = 1.$$

Equating real and imaginary parts we obtain

$$\int_\alpha^\beta e^{-ux} \cdot cos(vx) \cdot S(x) \cdot \phi_x^f \, dx = 1 \tag{D.7a}$$

and

$$\int_\alpha^\beta e^{-ux} \cdot sin(vx) \cdot S(x) \cdot \phi_x^f \, dx = 0. \tag{D.7b}$$

It follows that $u - iv$ is also a complex root of Equation (D.5), and the complex roots occur in conjugate pairs.

Because $cos(vx) < 1$ for some values of x in the range of integration for Equations (D.7), it follows that

$$\int_\alpha^\beta e^{-ux} \cdot S(x) \cdot \phi_x^f \, dx > 1. \tag{D.8a}$$

But

$$\int_\alpha^\beta e^{-r_0 x} \cdot S(x) \cdot \phi_x^f \, dx = 1, \tag{D.8b}$$

so $u < r_0$. This shows that $r_0 > Real\,(r_j)$. ▽

D.2 NUMERICAL VALUES OF r

Consider Equation (D.5), and define

$$R_i = \int_\alpha^\beta x^i \cdot S(x) \cdot \phi_x^f \, dx, \tag{D.9}$$

for $i = 0,1,2,\ldots$. R_0 is the average number of daughters that will be born to a female now aged 0, and it is known as the net reproduction rate (NRR). In general, R_0 is not equal to unity, and it is convenient to divide both sides of Equation (D.5) by R_0 to obtain

$$\int_\alpha^\beta \frac{e^{-r} \cdot S(x) \cdot \phi_x^f}{R_0} \, dx = \frac{1}{R_0}. \tag{D.10}$$

It is immediately apparent that $\dfrac{S(x) \cdot \phi_x^f}{R_0}$ is a probability density function in the range (α,β), and it follows that the left-hand side of Equation (D.10) is a moment generating function $M(-r)$. Taking logs of both sides, we obtain

$$K(-r) = -log\,R_0 + 2n\pi i, \tag{D.11}$$

for $n = 0,\pm1,\pm2,\ldots$, and $K(-r)$ is the cumulant generating function of the net maternity function of a stationary population.

The distribution is over the finite portion of the positive axis between α and β, so all the moments exist, and they are all finite. The cumulant generating function may be expanded in an infinite series to obtain

$$r\kappa_1 - \frac{1}{2!}\, r^2\kappa_2 + \frac{1}{3!}\, r\kappa_3 - \cdots = log\, R_0 - 2n\pi i. \qquad \text{(D.12)}$$

Equation (D.12) with $n=0$ is the one we now need to solve in order to evaluate r_0.

The material in Sections D.1 and D.2 follows Pollard [23].

D.3 THE RENEWAL EQUATION: APPLICATIONS IN RUIN THEORY AND DEMOGRAPHY

The equation

$$Z(x) = g(x) + \int_0^x Z(x-y)\cdot h(y)\, dy, \qquad \text{(D.13)}$$

for $x > 0$, is called a *renewal equation* and is important in ruin theory, a branch of actuarial mathematics.

The characteristic equation for the renewal process in a stable population is

$$\int_\alpha^\beta e^{-rx}\cdot S(x)\cdot\phi_x^f\, dx = 1. \qquad \text{(D.5)}$$

A similar equation,

$$\int_0^\infty e^{Ry}\cdot h(y)\, dy = 1, \qquad \text{(D.14)}$$

arises in ruin theory. If R is positive the equation is said to be defective, and if R is negative the equation is said to be excessive. Note that the variable R, called the adjustment coefficient in ruin theory, is analogous to the variable r in the mathematics of demography, the intrinsic rate of increase.

For more on renewal equations, the interested reader is referred to Gerber [10].

ANSWERS TO THE EXERCISES

Chapter 1

1-7 10

1-9 $C_X = 50,000;$ $C_Y = 25,000;$ $C_Z = 60,000$

1-10 $-.0646\%$

1-11 2-6 and 7-1

1-12 -6%; No

1-13 9.63%

1-14 4-8 and 9-3

1-15 1; 8

1-16 (a) 110,000   (b) 114,500   (c) 3.93%

Chapter 2

2-1 .18182

2-2 48,856

2-3 (a) .00755   (b) .00735   (c) .00724

2-4 .03292

2-5 .18730

2-6 Treatment A

2-7 .01119

2-8 .00600

2-9   10,236

2-10   .01000

2-11   .14791;   .14444

2-12   .11818;   .18636

2-13   .29834

2-14   (a) .01800   (b) .01000

2-15   .10000

2-16   (d) only

2-17   (a) 1.63595   (b) .79770   (c) .78561

2-18   (a) 6.50000   (b) 3.56800

2-19   .00900

2-20   .14894

2-21   .00816

Chapter 3

3-1   (a) and (b)

x	m_x	q_x	ℓ_x	d_x	p_x	L_x	T_x	$\overset{\circ}{e}_x$
0	.05	.049	1000	49	.951	976	3330	3.330
1	.10	.095	951	90	.905	906	2354	2.475
2	.30	.261	861	225	.739	748	1448	1.682
3	.50	.400	636	254	.600	509	700	1.101
4	2.00	1.000	382	382	.000	191	191	.500
5	--	--	0	--	--	--	--	--

(c) 5

3-2   (a) 364   (b) .33123   (c) .40168

3-3   (a).00104   (b).99866   (c).00043   (d).00068   (e)499.15335

3-4 $_tp_x(\mu_x - \mu_{x+t})$

3-6   .07146

3-7 $\quad \ell_0\left(\dfrac{100-x}{100}\right)$

3-9 $\quad -\dfrac{1}{\overset{\circ}{e}_x}$

3-10 $\quad \ell_x\left(\dfrac{T_x}{T_0}\right)^{.08}$

3-12

x	q_x	ℓ_x	d_x	p_x	L_x	T_x	$\overset{\circ}{e}_x$
0	.200	1000	200	.800	900	2010	2.0100
1	.400	800	320	.600	640	1110	1.3880
2	.600	480	288	.400	336	470	.9792
3	.800	192	154	.200	115	134	.6979
4	1.000	38	38	.000	19	19	.5000

3-13   .04877

3-14   (a) .51852   (b) .50341

3-16   (a) .01405   (b) .01410

3-17   (a) 19.32885   (b) 19.31956

Chapter 4

4-1   98,274;   95,409;   93,993;   90,348

4-2   .00094

4-3   .18727

4-4   .00503

4-5   .21909

4-6   2.84615

4-7   .00898

4-8   (a) 25,952   (b) 27,838   (c) .00442

4-9   (a) 28,140   (b) 24,040   (c) 23,050   (d) .03668

4-10   .01875

4-11   (a) 5000   (b) 72   (c) .04158

4-12   .00043

4-13   .00186

4-14   .42276

4-15   30.12040

4-16   (a) .09524   (b) .09552

4-17   7

4-18   58.91089, using UDD; 50.00000, without approximation

4-19   (a) .02469   (b) .01980

4-20   (a) .00337   (b) .86393   (c) 50.00000   (d) 88.04920

4-21   .97222

4-22   .94574

Chapter 5

5-1 $40 + \dfrac{T_{40} - T_{65} - 25\ell_{65}}{\ell_{40} - \ell_{65}}$

5-2   16.66667

5-3   40

5-4   (a) 116   (b) 1.16000

5-5   (a) $\dfrac{3000}{\ell_{25}}\left(T_{25} - .20T_{35} - .08T_{45} - .72T_{65}\right)$

       (b) $\dfrac{3000}{\ell_{25}}\left(.08\ell_{45}\right)$ (c) $\dfrac{3000}{\ell_{25}}\left(.72T_{65}\right)$

5-7   (a) $\dfrac{1000\ell_{25}}{T_{25} - .25T_{60} - .25T_{62} - .50T_{65}}$

       (b) $\dfrac{1000(\ell_{25} - .25\ell_{60} - .25\ell_{62} - .50\ell_{65})}{T_{25} - .25T_{60} - .25T_{62} - .50T_{65}}$

5-8   1889

5-9   50

5-10   800

5-11   .05996

5-12   .48049

5-13   6400

5-14   24,158

5-15 $20 + \dfrac{Y_{20} - Y_{65} - 45\,T_{65}}{T_{20} - T_{65}}$

5-16 $T_{30} - T_{40} + 10\ell_{30} - 20\ell_{65}$

5-17 $10\ell_{65} - 5\ell_{75} - T_{70} + T_{75}$

5-18 $10\ell_{65} - 5\ell_{75} - T_{70} + T_{75}$

5-19   (a) $T_{25} - T_{27} - T_{30} + T_{32}$ (b) $65 + \dfrac{T_{65} - T_{70} - 5\ell_{70}}{\ell_{65} - \ell_{70}}$

      (c) $Y_{25} - Y_{27} - 2T_{30} - 8\ell_{30}$

5-21   (a) $\dfrac{2000}{\ell_{21}}\Big(T_{21} - .20\,T_{55} - .80\,T_{65}\Big)$ (b) $\dfrac{2000}{\ell_{21}}\Big(.20\,T_{55} + .80\,T_{65}\Big)$

      (c) $\dfrac{2000}{\ell_{21}}(4000\,T_{55} + 24{,}000\,T_{65})$

5-22   (a) $\dfrac{100(T_{20} - T_{65})}{T_{65}}$ (b) 45

Chapter 6

6-1   .75000

6-2   16.66667

6-3   (a) .02500   (b) .01500

6-5   .01500

6-6   .01718

6-7   7164

6-8   1

6-9   .01257

6-10   (a) 6.00000   (b) 2.67600   (c) 2.52915

6-11   .02169

6-12   .02970

6-13   (a) .01116   (b) .01107

6-14   30.21000

6-15   (a) 1.51034   (b) 26.53130   (c) .01571

6-16   .74508

6-17   (a) .00283   (b) .00233

6-18   .02790

6-19   .17201

6-20   1.39967

6-21   1.08927

6-22   .34997

6-23   .05400

6-24   (a) 67,207   (b) 104,000

6-25   .46209

6-26   .60000

6-27   .06000

6-28   − 60.74844

6-29   .01492

6-30   .75000

6-31   13,258,974

6-32   4305.16022

6-33   2,643,079

6-34   (a) .01177   (b) .00667

6-35   .01677

Chapter 7

7-1   7.788%

7-2   .01278

7-3   .00003

7-4   708.29

7-5   2375 B.C.

7-6   (a) .02500   (b) .01748   (c) .01733

7-7   11,160,562

7-8   28,153,421

7-9   27,276,345

7-10 24,920,295

7-11 64,280,271

7-12 (a) 29,584,906   (b) .06108   (c) 17.86376

7-13 .00400

7-14 (a) 284,080,000   (b) 55.25272

7-15 $e^{-7.4}$

7-16 6.66667

7-17 33,333,333

7-18 (a) .04762   (b) No convergence to a single value

7-19 432,642

7-20 1,534,050

7-21 (a) 30,332,800   (b) 1.50987   (c) .47598

7-22 18,276

7-23 .00890

7-24 4.10000

7-25 1.63218

7-26 (a) .01267   (b) 1.39458   (c) 26.25046   (d) .30627

7-27 .12000

7-28   .21739

7-29   .01352

7-30   86

7-31   (a) $\begin{bmatrix} 5359.37 \\ 53.59 \\ 53.59 \end{bmatrix}$ (b) $\begin{bmatrix} 4923.77 \\ 3153.54 \\ 774.32 \end{bmatrix}$ (c) $\begin{bmatrix} 2763.21 \\ 316.17 \\ 36.71 \end{bmatrix}$

7-32 $\begin{bmatrix} .8 & .4 \\ .5 & 0 \end{bmatrix}$

Chapter 8

8-1   (a) .58333   (b) .50000   (c) 1.08333

8-2   2.08333

8-3   (a) 1.000; .976; .966; .943; 1.125; 1.362; 1.387   (b) .00547

8-4   No, because the immigrants are in the same age range as the Baby Boomers.

8-6   .01067

8-7   1.07338

8-8   (a) .02025   (b) .01015

8-9   .09090

8-10   .08000

BIBLIOGRAPHY

1. Annual Report of the Board of Trustees of the Federal OASDI Trust Fund, April 26, 1989. Washington: U.S. Government Printing Office, 1989.

2. Bogue, D.J., *Principles of Demography*. New York: John Wiley & Sons, 1969.

3. Bourgeois-Pichot, J., "The Concept of a Stable Population: Application to the Study of Populations of Countries with Incomplete Demographic Statistics," Population Studies No. 39, United Nations, 1968.

4. Bowers, N.L., et al., *Actuarial Mathematics*. Itasca: Society of Actuaries, 1986.

5. Brown, R.L., *Economic Security in an Aging Population*. Toronto: Butterworths Canada, 1991.

6. Brown, R.L., and B.W. Lutek, Discussion of "Geometric Solutions to Stationary Population Problems," by B. Chan, *TSA*, XXXIII (1981), 606.

7. Cox, P.R., *Demography*, 4th Ed. Cambridge: Cambridge University Press, 1970.

8. Easterlin, R.A., "What Will 1984 be Like? Socioeconomic Implications of Recent Twists in Age Structure," *Demography* 15(4), 397.

9. Ermisch, J.F., *The Political Economy of Demographic Change*. London: Heinemann Books, 1983.

10. Gerber, H.U., *An Introduction to Mathematical Risk Theory*. Homewood: Richard D. Irwin, Inc., 1979.

11. Grace, W.L. and C.J. Nesbitt, "Actuarial Note: On Average Age at Death Problems," *TSA*, II (1950), 70.

12. Jordan, C.W., *Life Contingencies.* Chicago: Society of Actuaries, 1967.

13. Kettle, J., *The Big Generation.* Toronto: McClelland and Stewart, 1980.

14. Keyfitz, N., *Introduction to the Mathematics of Population*, with Revisions. Reading: Addison-Wesley, 1977.

15. _____, *Applied Mathematical Demography.* New York: John Wiley & Sons, 1977.

16. Keyfitz, N. and J.A. Beekman, *Demography Through Problems.* New York: Springer-Verlag, 1977.

17. Keyfitz, N., and W. Flieger, *Population Facts and Methods of Demography.* San Francisco: W.H. Freeman & Company, 1971.

18. Keyfitz, N. and D.P. Smith, *Mathematical Demography.* New York: Springer-Verlag, 1977.

19. London, D., *Graduation: The Revision of Estimates.* Winsted: ACTEX Publications, 1985.

20. _____, *Survival Models and Their Estimation.* Winsted: ACTEX Publications, 1988.

21. Myers, R.J., "Errors and Bias in the Reporting of Ages in Census Data," TASA, XLI (1940), 395.

22. Pollard, A.H., F. Yusuf, and G.N. Pollard, *Demographic Techniques*, 3rd Ed. Sydney: Pergamon Press, 1990.

23. Pollard, J.H., *Mathematical Models for the Growth of Human Populations.* Cambridge: Cambridge University Press, 1973.

24. Spiegleman, M., *Introduction to Demography*, Rev. Ed. Cambridge: Harvard University Press, 1968.

25. Statistics Canada, "Current Demographic Analysis." Ottawa: Ministry of Supply and Services, 1989.

26. Statistics Canada, "Catalogue 91-520: Population Projections for Canada, Provinces and Territories." Ottawa: Ministry of Supply and Services, 1985.

27. U.S. Bureau of the Census, "International Population Reports Series P-95, No. 78: An Aging World." Washington: Department of Commerce, 1987.

28. U.S. Public Health Service, "Vital Statistics of the United States." Washington: Department of Health and Human Services, 1989.

29. Veit, K.P., "Stationary Population Methods," *TSA*, XVI (1964), 233.

INDEX